HEY, TRUE CRIME LOVER, I KNOW WHO YOU ARE

You're the one who relaxes while watching a crime and murder show. The one who likes to tickle the nerves with the details of terrible occasions. The one interested in how the brains of serial killers work and why they are so different from us.

And that's OK. You are OK!

It's OK to want to learn as much as possible about terrible crimes to become more careful and learn how to protect yourself and your loved ones.

We made this True Crime Activity Book for everyone who wants to know more about the terrible murders that the most high-profile criminals in the world committed. To prolong the intrigue and find out some facts, you will have to solve some tasks: cryptograms, word scrambles, tests, fallen phrases, word searches, and much more.

In this book, you will find what you wanted to know about the crimes of notorious serial killers.

Remember that the information contained in this book is provided on an "as is" basis with no guarantees of completeness, accuracy, usefulness, or timeliness. We do not support murder, violence, or the actions of the characters depicted in this book.

HOW TO SOLVE TRUE CRIME WORD SEARCH

Your task is to find the hidden words related to real crime in the letter puzzle. Just run a finger along each row in turn, stopping at every instance of the first letter in the elusive word. When found, run your finger around to the adjacent letters in every direction, looking for the second, then third letters in the word.

HOW TO SOLVE SUDOKU

You need to fill in all the cells with numbers using the following rules: Every square has to contain a single number; only the numbers 1 through 9 can be used; each 3 × 3 box can only contain each number from 1 to 9 once; each vertical column can only contain each number from 1 to 9 once.

HOW TO SOLVE FALLEN PHRASE

You complete the puzzle by filling the letters into the column they fall under: you start by filling in the one-letter columns because those clearly don't have anywhere else to go in their column. Also the key is filling in common one-, two- and three-letter words.

HOW TO SOLVE WORD TILE

We chose the full name of one serial killer. Your task is to put together as many different words as possible from their letters. For example, from the name Ted Bundy, you can add the words buddy, debut, bed, and so on.

HOW TO SOLVE MAZE

Find a way out of the maze and save the victim from the bloodthirsty killer! You need to draw a continuous line with a pencil or pen from the victim who is in the center to the exit, avoiding dead ends.

HOW TO SOLVE COLORING PAGE

Come on! Haven't you tried coloring yet? We have a stunning Bloody Alphabet series featuring the most terrifying serial killers. Just pick up pencils, paints, crayons or whatever and color the picture to your liking!

HOW TO SOLVE WHAT IS COMMON BETWEEN TWO SERIAL KILLERS

Think carefully and re-read the biographies of the two killers shown in the picture. You need to find several things that unite them. These can either be personal issues or facts from life or coincidences in dates. Remember that there are answers at the end of the book.

HOW TO SOLVE MATH LOGIC

To solve math logic, just guess which numbers are hidden behind the images and write down the answer to the equation.

Remember that the same images = the same numbers.

HOW TO SOLVE RIDDLES

In front of you is a picture of a murder. Your task is to see the smallest evidence and guess which famous killer committed this murder. Take a thorough look and remember the facts about the notorious killers.

HOW TO SOLVE CROSSWORDS

Read the question in each task and write the answer in the boxes under the corresponding number, letter by letter.

HOW TO SOLVE CRYPTOGRAMS

You will see an encrypted phrase with some random letters. The beginning of the phrase will be deciphered, so you will already know which letters. Next, you need to take the encoded message, figure out
what letters are substituted, and the meaning of the cryptogram using the word patterns. We advise you to start with small words, such as articles or prepositions. Keep guessing the message ideas until you solve the secret code. And remember: each letter represents one certain letter.

CAN YOU NAME A THING

RELATED TO TRUE CRIME FOR EVERY LETTER OF THE ALPHABET

A ______________________________

B ______________________________

C ______________________________

D ______________________________

E ______________________________

F ______________________________

J ______________________________

H ______________________________

I ______________________________

J ______________________________

K ______________________________

L ______________________________

M ______________________________

CAN YOU NAME A THING

RELATED TO TRUE CRIME FOR EVERY LETTER OF THE ALPHABET

N ______________________________

O ______________________________

P ______________________________

Q ______________________________

R ______________________________

S ______________________________

T ______________________________

U ______________________________

V ______________________________

W ______________________________

X ______________________________

Y ______________________________

Z ______________________________

TRUE CRIME MEMES
THAT ABSOLUTELY DROVE OUR INSTAGRAM FOLLOWERS CRAZY

Me on a Date Trying to Find the Right
Moment to Start Talking About Serial Killers

THAT TESTS

What Irrefutable Evidence Does Law Enforcement Have About the Delphi Case, Even Though the Case Has Not Been Resolved For More Than Four Years?

a. Video and sound of the voice

b. The photo

c. Physical evidence with the DNA

LEVEL 1

Imagine being caught by a serial killer, but you have a chance to get out of captivity! To do so, you need to find a way out of the center of the labyrinth in one minute. Schedule the time and see if you have a chance to be saved!

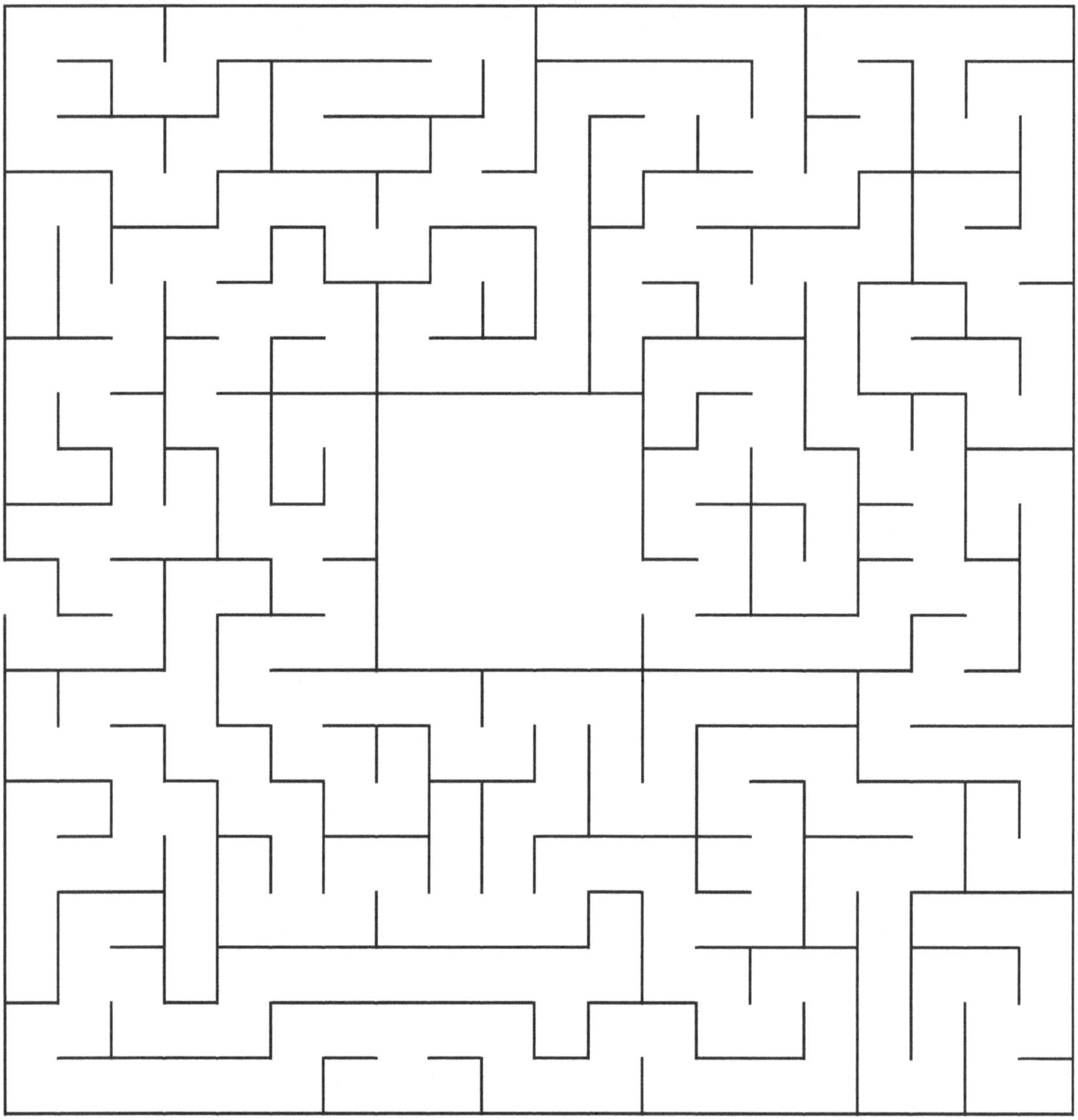

EXPRESS YOUR OPINION

Rate the worst people in the world - serial killers who don't even deserve to live in prisons

1. ______________________
2. ______________________
3. ______________________
4. ______________________
5. ______________________
6. ______________________
7. ______________________
8. ______________________
9. ______________________
10. ______________________
11. ______________________
12. ______________________
13. ______________________

SUDOKU

		7					6	2
5			1			7		
				5				
	4			8			7	
2			4			1		
9		8	3		1		2	5
	6		9					
7	3	9					1	
8			6			2		3

Oh no, not these facts again!

Richard Ramirez became "The Valley Intruder" when his crimes were first reported in the media. As Ramirez's reign of terror progressed, people agreed that "Valley Intruder" was not the right fit, and he became "The Night Stalker."

Create as many words as you can.

HERMAN WEBSTER MUDGETT

I WISH I DIDN'T KNOW THAT TESTS

What did Jeffrey Dahmer do with the bodies of some of the murdered victims?

a. Moved them into the concrete walls of his house

b. Cooked and ate them

c. Dismembered them into small pieces and threw them into the river

EXPRESS YOUR OPINION

Make a list of things you are afraid of

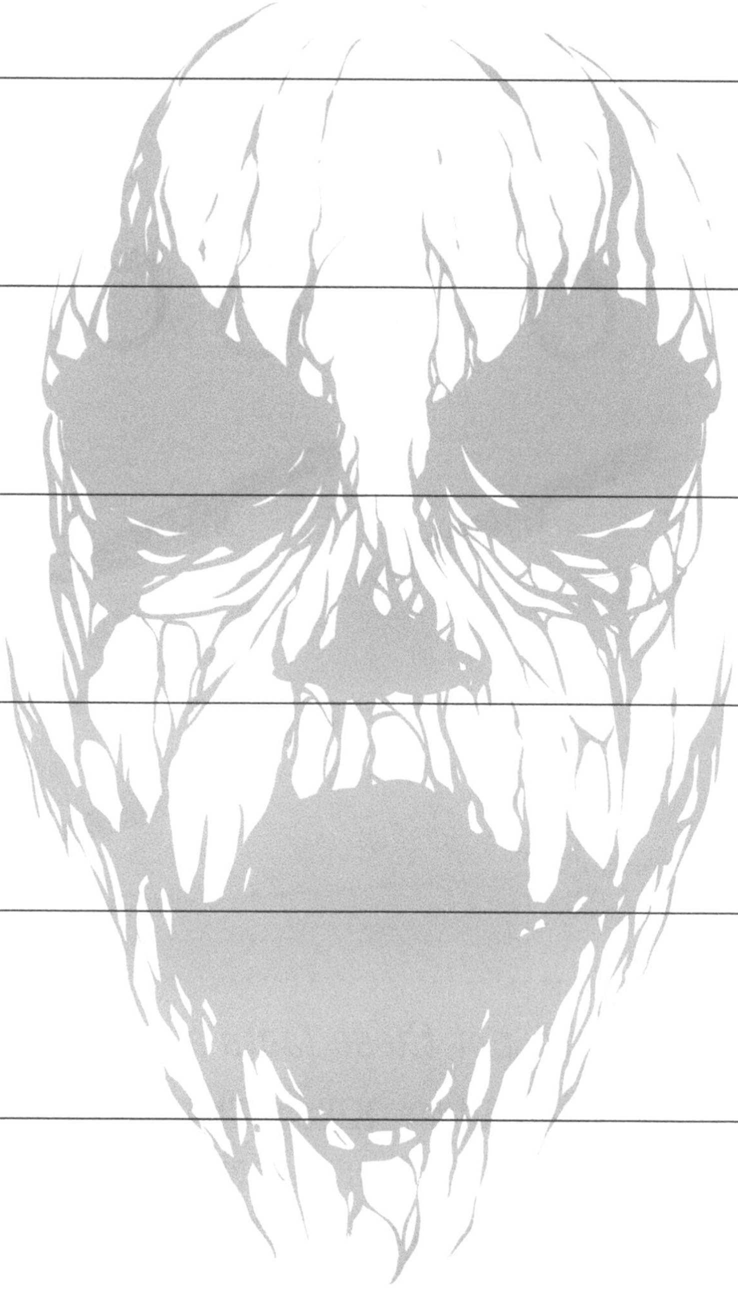

1. ______________________________

2. ______________________________

3. ______________________________

4. ______________________________

5. ______________________________

6. ______________________________

7. ______________________________

MATH LOGIC

Are you good at math?
Solve this true crime riddle

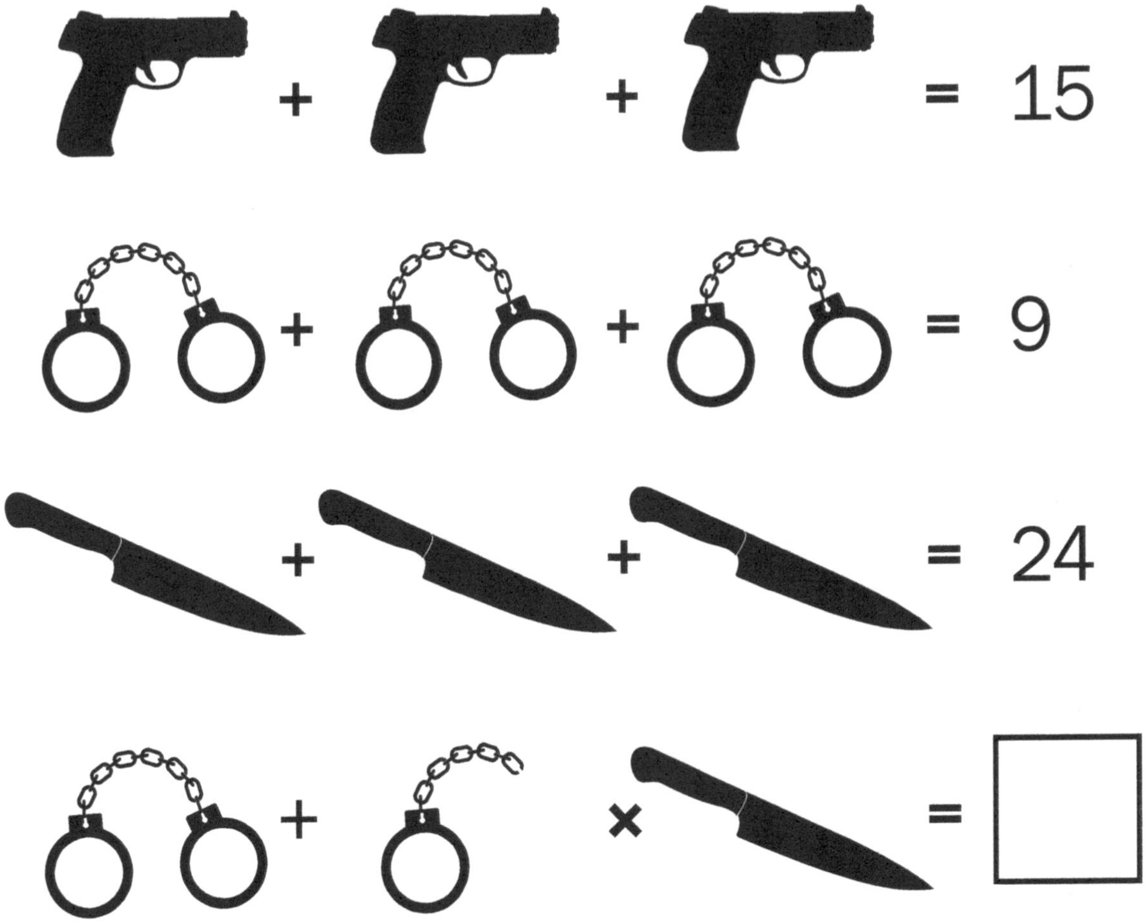

+ + = 15

+ + = 9

+ + = 24

+ × = ☐

Oh no, not these facts again!

The BTK Killer, The Green River Killer, The Sunday Morning Slasher, The Casanova Killer. What do these serial killers have in common besides their ominous pseudonyms? They started killing in 1974. John Wayne Gacy also murdered his second victim in 1974.

TRUE CRIME MEMES
THAT ABSOLUTELY DROVE OUR INSTAGRAM FOLLOWERS CRAZY

Reality

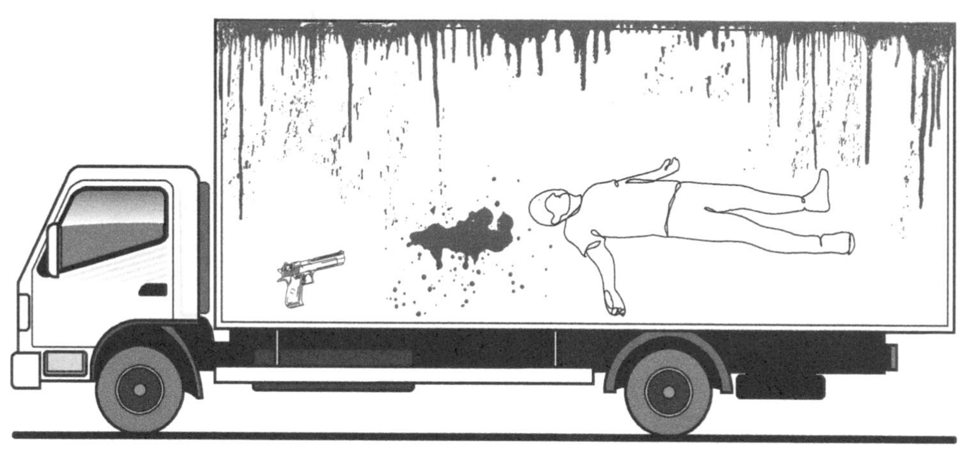

What A True Crime Fan Sees

Oh no, not these facts again!

Jeffrey Dahmer drilled holes in some of his victims' heads while they were alive and poured acid in the holes because he wanted to make "sex zombies" out of them.

RIDDLES

Guess who committed this crime. Be attentive to the smallest details and remember the biographies of the most well-known serial killers!

KILLER'S NAME: ______________________________

COLORING PAGES
Elizabeth
Bathory
1560-1614
650
BÁTHORY,
ELIZABETH

Connect letters to rearrange them into other words!

Create as many words as you can

GERARD JOHN SCHAEFER

FALLEN PHRASES!

"		■					E			■				■			L	Y	■	W			■		
■							■			O	P	L	E	■			■			■			L		■
■	■	■	■	■	■	■	■	■		H		M	.	"	■	■	■	■	■	■	■	■	■	■	■
■	■	■	■	■	■	■				L	■		A						■	■	■	■	■	■	■

									E																
								P	T						Z	S									
	R		B	E	R	I		V	R		E	P			O	N		T			A	Y		L	
	I	E	F	O	L	M	C	A	E		T	H	E	N	I	R	A	M	O		K	I		T	O

Oh no, not these facts again!

Jeffrey Dahmer, who was convicted of 15 homicides, admitted to cooking and eating some of his victims. In fact, he even gave the people in his apartment building sandwiches, which may have contained his victims' flesh.

I WISH I DIDN'T KNOW

THAT TESTS

What serial killers did his own daughter help to uncover?

a. Albert Fish

b. Ed Gein

c. Dennis Rader

CROSSWORDS

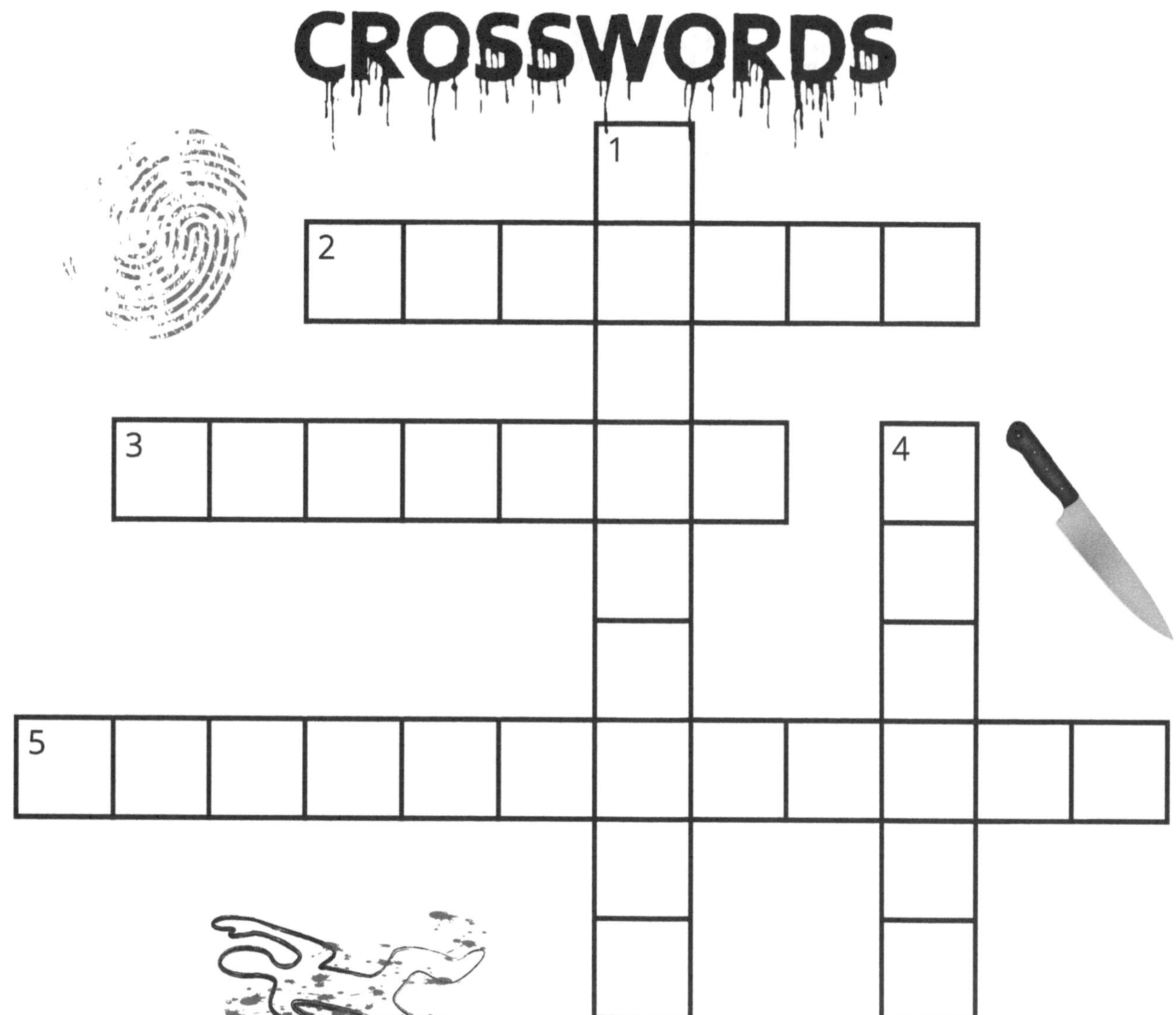

DOWN:

1. The Boston ... was a nickname of Albert de Salvo

4. Which serial killer was the inspiration for the murderous character of Scorpio in the 1971 film Dirty Harry?

ACROSS:

2. How old was Edmund Kemper when he first committed murder?

3. The surname of a serial killer that Ted Bundy helped detectives catch

5. What was Ted Bundy's education?

EXPRESS YOUR OPINION

For 24 hours, murder is legal.
Who are you killing first?
Make a list and don't be afraid to share your secret thoughts!

1. ______________________________

2. ______________________________

3. ______________________________

4. ______________________________

5. ______________________________

6. ______________________________

7. ______________________________

WORD SCRAMBLE

Hidden in each of these word scrambles are the names of the most famous female murderers that begin with B.
Find all of them!

1. aBlrefid ______________________________

2. atnbeaBr ______________________________

3. Bcke ______________________________

4. eenBdr ______________________________

5. nwrBo ______________________________

6. uneooaBn ______________________________

7. uyBnd ______________________________

Oh no, not these facts again!

Ed Gein is one of the most popular serial killers in America and it is quite amazing that he killed only two people.

COLORING PAGES

SHIPMAN, HAROLD

215-265+

TAXI

TRUE CRIME MEMES

THAT ABSOLUTELY DROVE OUR INSTAGRAM FOLLOWERS CRAZY

How Serial Killers Who Haven't Been Caught Watch A Documentary About Their Crimes

Oh no, not these facts again!

Although the FBI believes that there are as many as 25 active serial killers in America right now, researchers at the Murder Accountability Project have disagreed. Their findings reveal that the number of serial killers might be close to 2,000.

Unjumble the scrambled letters to make surnames of the serial killers with the largest number of victims

1. VITRGAOA ______________________
2. ZOLPE ______________________
3. AQBLI ______________________
4. VKPOPO ______________________
5. RASABBO ______________________
6. OLIFH ______________________
7. SAAAINKRHY ______________________

Oh no, not these facts again!

The largest mass-murder in the history of the United States of America happened on October 1, 2018, during a concert in Las Vegas. Gunman Stephen Paddock had turned the gun on himself after killing 58 people and leaving another 851 terribly injured. From the first pull of the trigger to the last, Paddock's massacre lasted for up to 10 minutes.

Guess who committed this crime. Be attentive to the smallest details and remember the biographies of the most well-known serial killers!

KILLER'S NAME: ______________________________

CRYPTOGRAMS

In his biography, this freak has collected all the most terrible murders that occurred in the most sophisticated ways: dismemberment, necrophilia, cannibalism, a home cemetery with corpses... He could not just die without saying these intriguing words in the end. Do you want to know the last phrase of the killer of 17 men? Then solve this cryptogram!

A	B	C	D	E	F	G	H	I	J	K	L	M	N	O	P	Q	R	S	T	U	V	W	X	Y	Z

I		D	O	N'	T		C	A	R	E										
P		K	V	U	A		J	H	Y	L		P	M		P		S	P	C	L

V	Y		K	P	L		N	V		H	O	L	H	K		H	U	K

R	P	S	S		T	L

4	2	7	5	1	3	9	8	6
9	6	3	8				7	5
	8	5	7			3		
		4	6	3	1			
6	7	1		8	9			
2	3	8	4	7	5		1	9
3	4	2		6				7
8	1		9			2		4

Oh no, not these facts again!

When we give nicknames to serial killers, we often accidentally elevate them to mythic status, turning them into romantic figures. This is not the case with Robert Nixon, also known as "The Brick Moron."

MATH LOGIC

Are you good at math? Solve this true crime riddle

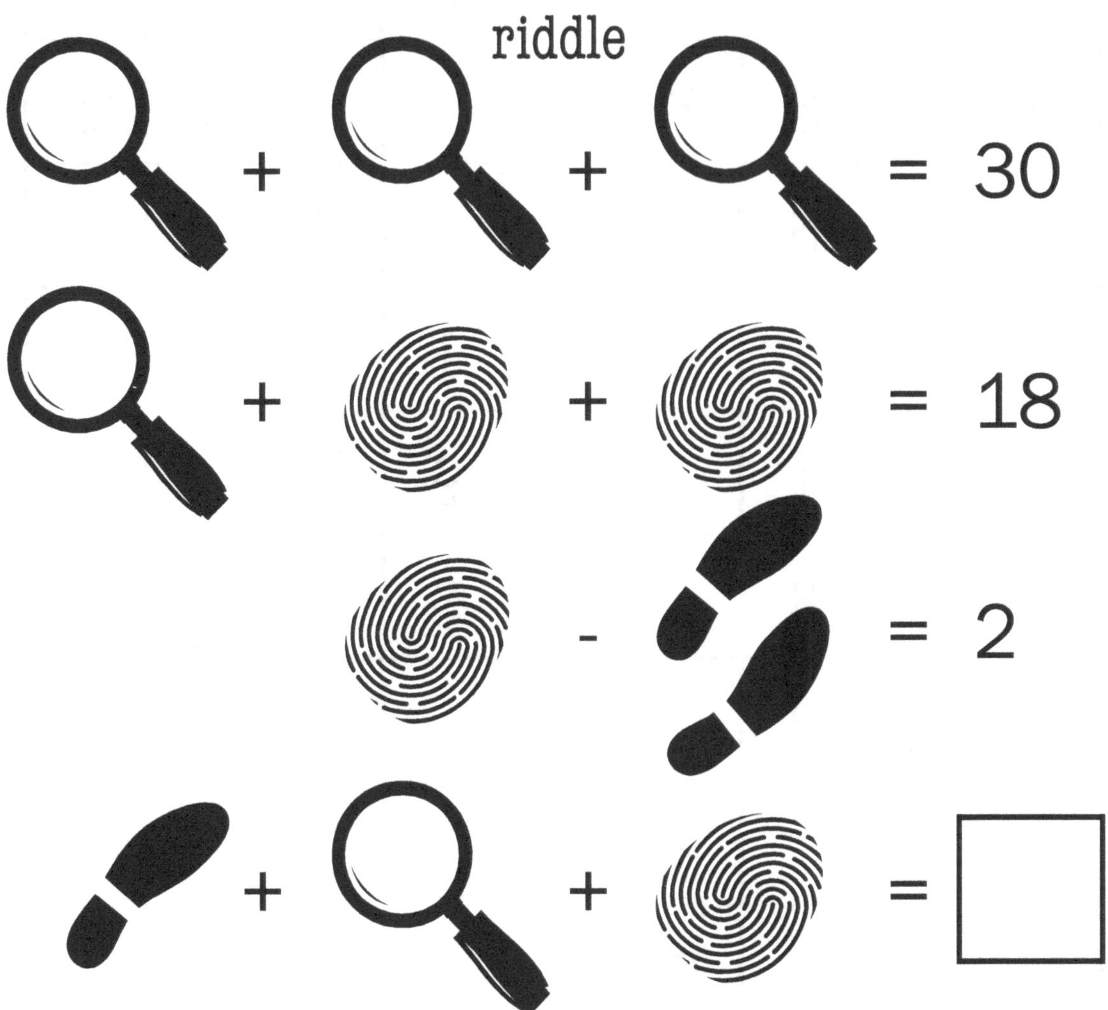

Oh no, not these facts again!

Mass killings are on the rise. The five deadliest mass shootings in US history have all occurred in the last ten years. 53.8% of the serial killers' victims were women, and 15% were chosen at random; that means 85% of victims were specifically chosen.

Connect letters to rearrange them into other words! Create as many words as you can

ANATOLY ONOPRIENKO

I WISH I DIDN'T KNOW

THAT TESTS

How many years did it take the authorities to catch the Golden State Killer?

a. 20 years

b. 30 years

c. 40 years

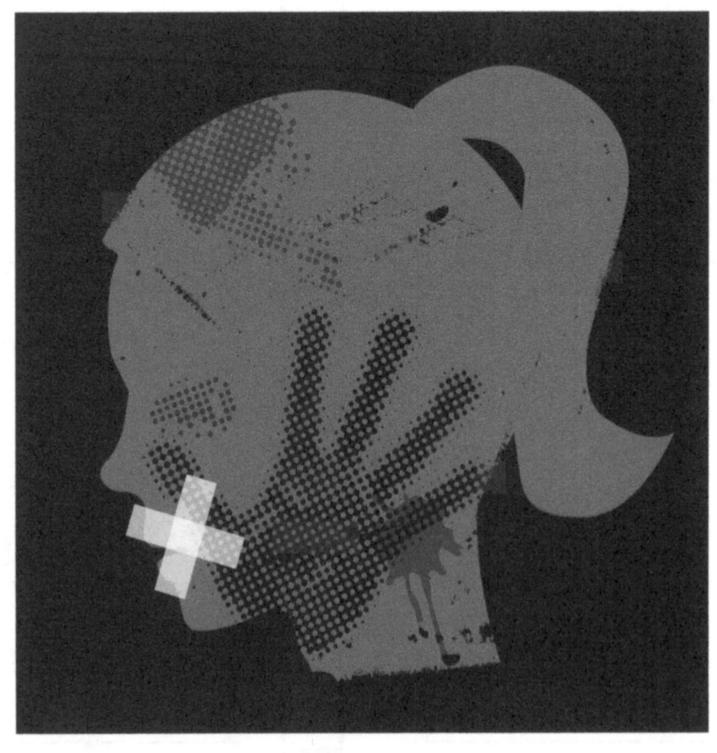

COLORING PAGES
ALLANSON, PATRICIA
1-3
POISON
ARSENIOUS AC

TRUE-CRIME WORD SEARCH

Find 12 serial killers that are Capricorns. BTW, this zodiac sign is inherent in many serial killers!

N	S	S	R	J	D	L	I	L	S	G	H	C	C
E	R	S	K	I	N	E	K	N	O	T	L	R	A
D	L	E	I	F	D	O	O	W	O	O	E	I	C
O	N	O	S	N	I	B	O	R	O	O	E	O	N
T	D	S	I	N	M	B	H	L	L	R	O	C	A
B	A	N	J	O	A	S	H	I	P	M	A	N	M
N	O	S	D	H	S	F	L	E	K	L	S	R	Y
L	K	T	A	O	S	D	I	S	D	T	N	J	D
S	T	T	R	G	G	N	O	L	S	V	E	I	N
R	J	N	U	E	O	E	L	S	O	O	M	L	A
D	T	M	S	L	A	P	E	T	I	O	T	E	C
A	F	S	O	D	S	E	M	O	A	R	A	A	L
P	M	S	M	I	L	A	T	S	L	I	V	K	O
D	M	L	K	E	Y	E	S	L	G	F	I	E	Y

My Best Friend And I Watching A Bloody Documentary For 10 Hours Straight

Oh no, not these facts again!

Only 15% of serial killers' victims are chosen at random, which means that 85% of the victims were specifically chosen. Also, it is a known fact that 50% of serial killers list pleasure as their primary motive in murder.

CAN YOU NAME A TRUE CRIME

TV SHOW/PODCAST/BOOK FOR EVERY LETTER OF THE ALPHABET

A ______________________________

B ______________________________

C ______________________________

D ______________________________

E ______________________________

F ______________________________

J ______________________________

H ______________________________

I ______________________________

J ______________________________

K ______________________________

L ______________________________

M ______________________________

CAN YOU NAME A TRUE CRIME

TV SHOW/PODCAST/BOOK FOR EVERY LETTER OF THE ALPHABET

N ______________________________

O ______________________________

P ______________________________

Q ______________________________

R ______________________________

S ______________________________

T ______________________________

U ______________________________

V ______________________________

W ______________________________

X ______________________________

Y ______________________________

Z ______________________________

COLORING PAGES
OGORZÓW, PAUL
8
S-BAHN MURDERER

CRYPTOGRAMS

Clown-rapist of young guys. Killer clown. Clown public figure, party member. This monster definitely deserves to die.

How about finding out his last words?

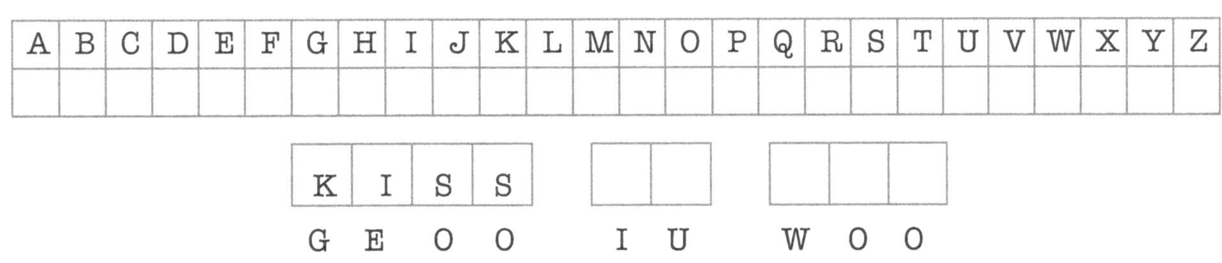

Connect letters to rearrange them into other words!
Create as many words as you can

STEPHEN DEE RICHARDS

TRUE CRIME MEMES
THAT ABSOLUTELY DROVE OUR INSTAGRAM FOLLOWERS CRAZY

Me Arriving At the True Crime Museum

Oh no, not these facts again!

Ted Bundy, America's most prolific serial killer, once worked at a suicide hotline and saved a three-year-old child from drowning in a pool.

LEVEL 2

How does it feel to run away from a maniac? It is similar to getting out of a maze. For example, this one. Imagine that you are in the center. Can you find a way out in one minute?

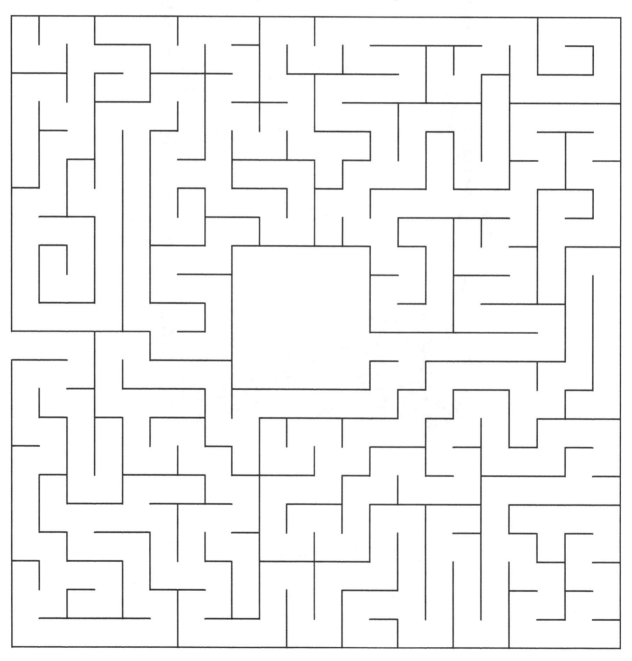

COLORING PAGES
FALLING CHRISTINE
6

Are you good at math? Solve this true crime riddle

+ + = 60

+ + = 40

+ + = 26

+ × = □

Oh no, not these facts again!

H.H. Holmes was the serial killer made famous by his "Murder Castle" where he killed his victims in the 1890s. He was later found to have sold the skeletons of his victims to medical schools for profit.

EXPRESS YOUR OPINION

Rank the record-breaking zodiac signs among serial killers, and then check out the answers at the end of the book. Now you will know which zodiac sign is the most popular among these bastards!

1. ______________________________

2. ______________________________

3. ______________________________

4. ______________________________

5. ______________________________

6. ______________________________

7. ______________________________

Unscramble these words to find the places where the most high-profile crimes in America took place.

LNOSAGEELS ____________________

AIMIM ____________________

ASLAAK ____________________

NATHREMSCE ____________________

WONMEEXIC ____________________

EESSNEENT ____________________

SNAASAKR ____________________

ENVDAA ____________________

SLUIINAOA ____________________

USIORSMI ____________________

What did the serial killer's mom (Isreal Keys) say when the cops asked her to help them find the missing girl?

a. If God wanted her found, she would be found

b. I will describe all the details about each of the victims

c. If I'd known about my son's double life, I would have told you earlier

EXPRESS YOUR OPINION

You are going to take part in a survival game against aliens.
You can assemble your team of five serial killers.
Who would you choose and why?

1.
2.
3.
4.
5.

WHAT IS IN COMMON

BETWEEN WUORNOS AND RAMIREZ?

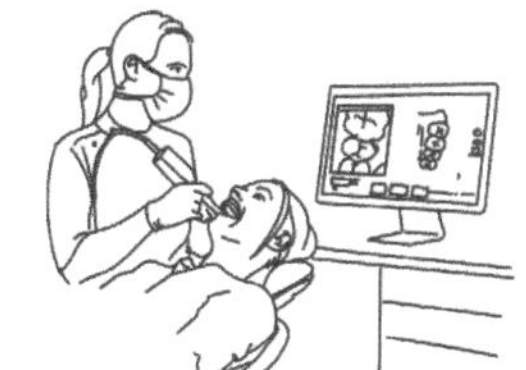

1. ____________________________________
2. ____________________________________
3. ____________________________________
4. ____________________________________
5. ____________________________________
6. ____________________________________
7. ____________________________________

RIDDLES

Guess who committed this crime. Be attentive to the smallest details and remember the biographies of the most well-known serial killers!

KILLER'S NAME: ______________________________

COLORING PAGES
27
HAARMANN, "FRITZ"

			6			5		
5			1			2		
				5			7	
	5		9	8		6		7
	7	6	4			9		8
			7	6				
			3	9	7			
7	4	2		1	8		6	
8						7		

TRUE CRIME MEMES

THAT ABSOLUTELY DROVE OUR INSTAGRAM FOLLOWERS CRAZY

When The Husband Of A Murdered Woman In A Documentary Says "I Love My Wife Very Much And Would Never Do Anything To Hurt Her."

Oh no, not these facts again!

Joel Rifkin was the most prolific serial killer in the history of New York. He murdered 17 women in just 2 years, and it is possible that he would have gotten away with it if not for a routine traffic stop. When the police tried to pull Rifkin over for expired tags, he fled and crashed his car during the chase. After he was caught, he admitted to having a dismembered body in his trunk.

Connect letters to rearrange them into other words! Create as many words as you can

CARL EUGENE WATTS

EXPRESS YOUR OPINION

What is an *unpopular* opinion you have about true crime cases? Write it down and don't be afraid to share your secret thoughts!

MATH LOGIC

Are you good at math? Solve this true crime riddle

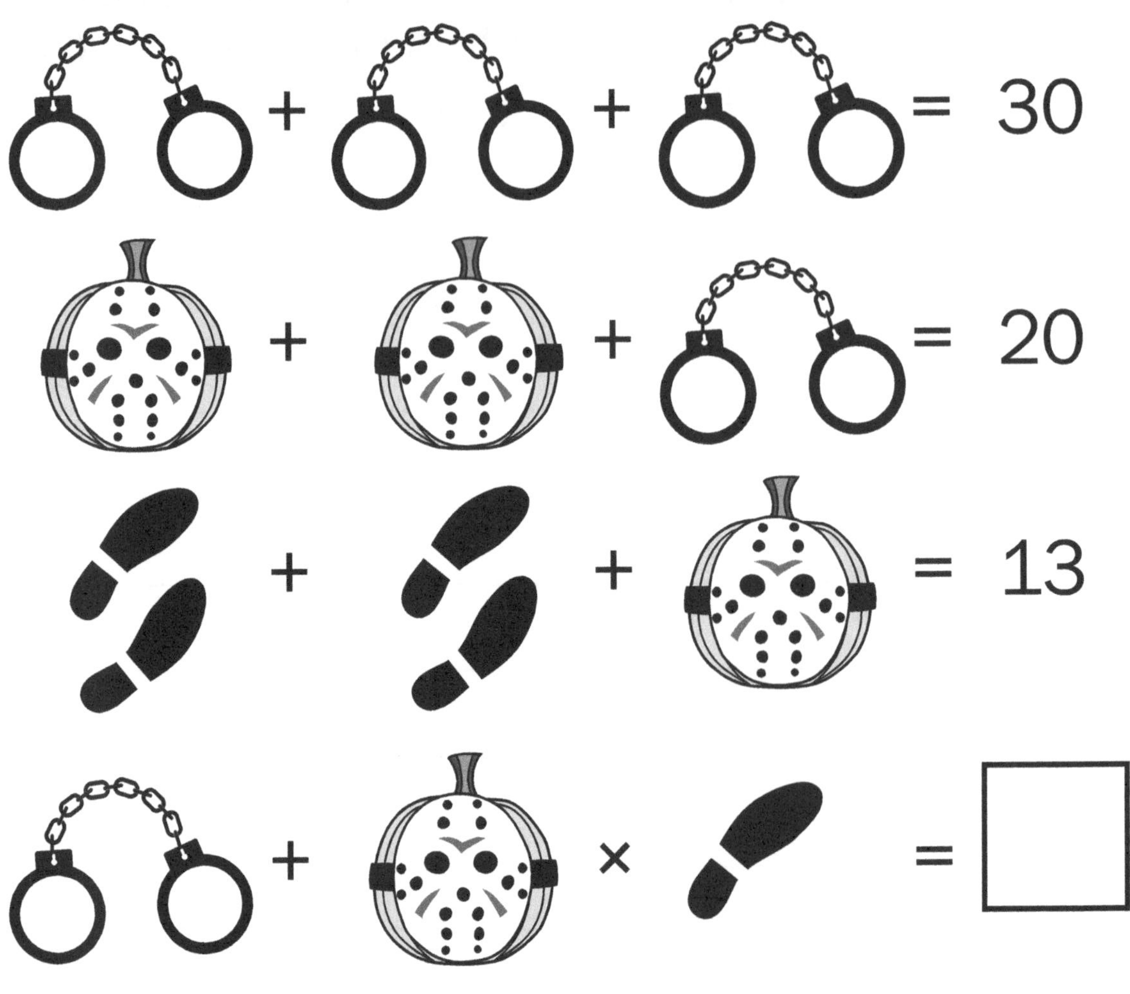

THE ANSWER IS ________________________

Oh no, not these facts again!

In 1922, 997 New Yorkers died of poisoning, and there's a high probability that these deaths were murder. It wasn't common practice to test for poisons during police investigations, and because coroners could be bribed easily, a serial killer might commit dozens of other poisonings and remain undetected.

I WISH I DIDN'T KNOW THAT TESTS

How did Jeffrey Dahmer describe the taste of human skin with tattoos?

a. Sweet taste

b. Tough and bitter

c. It tastes like shit

COLORING PAGES
CULLEN CHARLES
FIRE
MISSILES
29-35

Everybody: How Do You Sleep After Watching All Those Awful Documentaries About Murders?

Me:

TRUE-CRIME WORD SEARCH

Find 19 words related to crime! By the way, you can find all the answers in the last pages of the book.
But don't look there ahead of time!

M	T	E	V	K	I	D	N	A	P	P	I	N	G
U	U	S	P	T	I	E	C	P	O	H	T	R	E
R	Y	A	D	B	P	A	B	O	D	Y	I	M	L
D	R	C	A	N	P	T	A	Y	P	I	A	L	A
E	A	D	N	D	I	H	N	L	R	Y	O	S	T
R	C	L	G	C	R	I	M	E	O	N	C	I	E
B	S	O	E	L	E	S	E	I	I	E	L	A	N
L	N	C	R	P	B	L	S	M	E	V	U	K	T
O	R	H	R	L	B	E	U	E	E	I	S	C	P
O	N	O	T	I	E	L	R	S	M	L	S	V	R
D	S	E	R	I	A	L	K	I	L	L	E	R	I
L	R	R	E	F	I	N	K	O	L	T	E	L	N
I	E	E	J	U	S	T	I	C	E	N	S	N	T
T	B	D	S	N	B	K	C	T	S	E	R	R	A

CAN YOU NAME A SERIAL KILLER

FOR EVERY LETTER IN THE ALPHABET

A ______________________________

B ______________________________

C ______________________________

D ______________________________

E ______________________________

F ______________________________

J ______________________________

H ______________________________

I ______________________________

J ______________________________

K ______________________________

L ______________________________

M ______________________________

CAN YOU NAME A SERIAL KILLER

FOR EVERY LETTER IN THE ALPHABET

N ______________________________

O ______________________________

P ______________________________

Q ______________________________

R ______________________________

S ______________________________

T ______________________________

U ______________________________

V ______________________________

W ______________________________

X ______________________________

Y ______________________________

Z ______________________________

Connect letters to rearrange them into other words! Create as many words as you can

MARY FRANCES CREIGHTON

WORD SCRAMBLE

These horrible people were not just murderers but cannibals. However, they fucked up because they were caught by the police. Rearrange the letters in the words to find the names of these bastards.

1. IFSH ______________________________

2. SSARCHOSW ______________________________

3. OLKRL ______________________________

4. MEHDRA ______________________________

5. TOLOE ______________________________

6. ADLMSEYU ______________________________

7. OKIILAHCT

____

Oh no, not these facts again!

Journalist Vlado Taneski wrote two articles about the recent murder cases in town. He mentioned key and undisclosed details about the case that only the killer could know, and that was how he got caught.

CRYPTOGRAMS

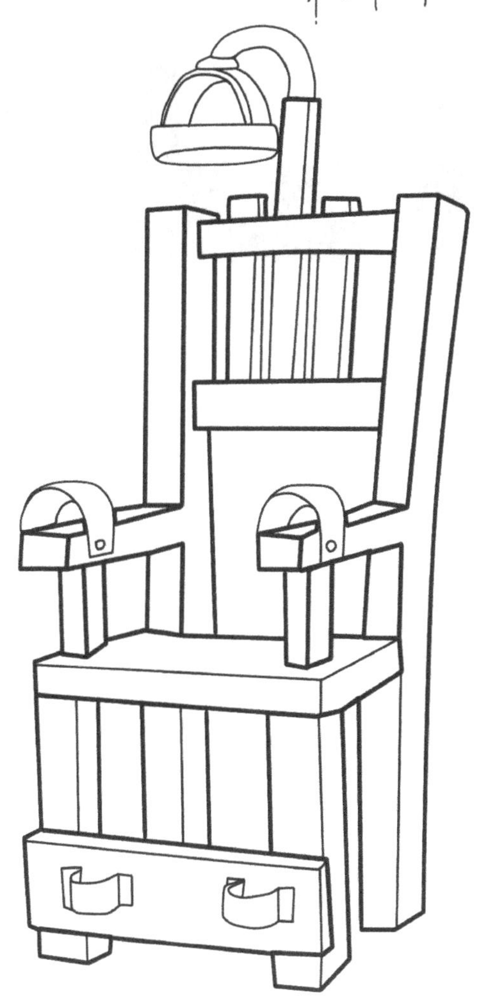

Execution by electric chair is perhaps one of the most terrible ways to leave this life. Police killer George Appel was not afraid, and even shouted a joke a moment before his death. Wanna know which one? Solve the cryptogram to find out.

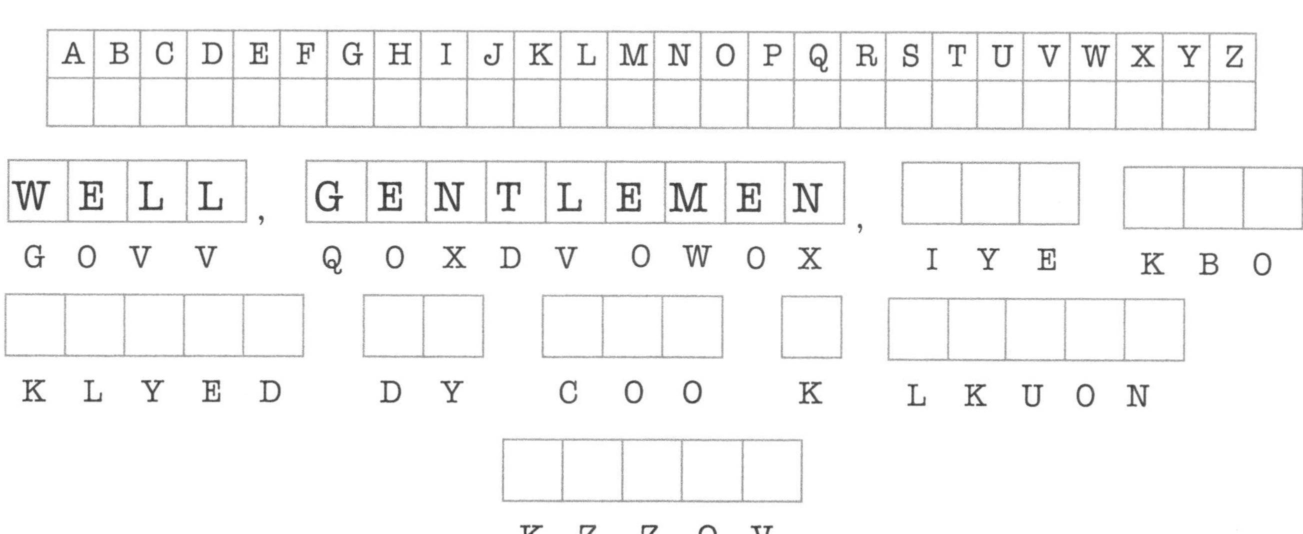

FALLEN PHRASES!

■	"	I	■									■	T	H				■		■				■		E	■	■
■			S							■		I		H	■		E					…		■				■
							■	O		■			■			A		■			■	A	■				.	"
■	■	■	■	■	■	■	■							■	R			E		■	■	■	■	■	■	■	■	■

D Y A

P E T E L M N D R I

R O S C D S D E N W Y T I D D I S S Y W A

D P O P A E S U A N L N I S H E A K M O N M A I K B D S

Oh no, not these facts again!

Robert Hansen killed 17 women in 12 years. He was known for kidnapping his victims and then setting them loose in the Knik River Valley, where he would track and hunt them like animals using a knife and rifle.

RIDDLES

Guess who committed this crime. Be attentive to the smallest details and remember the biographies of the most well-known serial killers!

KILLER'S NAME: ______________________________

WHAT IS IN COMMON

BETWEEN GACY AND FISH?

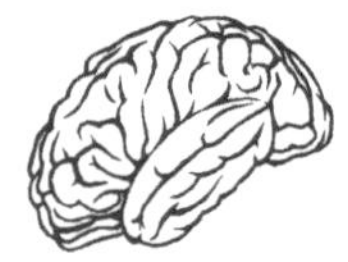

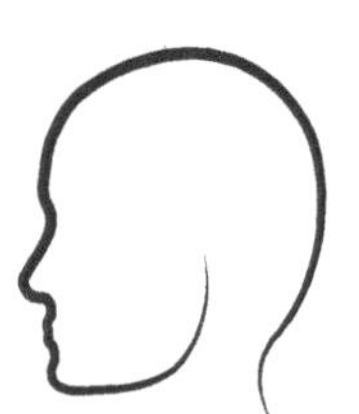

1. ______________________________

2. ______________________________

3. ______________________________

4. ______________________________

5. ______________________________

6. ______________________________

7. ______________________________

When Somebody Tells Me
He Wanna Learn More About True Crime

I Can Fix That

Oh no, not these facts again!

Serhiy Tkach was a Soviet soldier and a police forensics expert. His experience in this field allowed him to avoid the Ukrainian authorities for decades while he murdered more than 100 people and framed others for his crimes. He even attended the funerals of some of his victims.

		8			5	7		
		9	2					1
1	7						8	4
			3	8		1	4	5
4						9		
			6					
					2	4	5	8
6						3	2	

Oh no, not these facts again!

Mack Ray Edwards worked for Caltrans. He'd kill his victims and bury their bodies in places he was contracted to build highways over. Not all his victims have been found, and it is possible that many are still under some of the California highways you may have driven over countless times.

TRUE-CRIME WORD SEARCH

Oh yes, these bastards are completely sick! But what about a little psychological analysis? Find 17 psychological traits of serial killers

N	M	A	N	I	P	U	L	A	T	I	V	E	N
P	A	A	C	D	E	C	E	I	T	F	U	L	O
T	R	S	I	B	C	O	Y	H	T	A	P	M	E
G	S	L	U	E	V	I	S	L	U	P	M	I	L
L	O	A	C	A	L	L	O	U	S	N	E	S	S
I	N	I	P	N	A	N	R	E	M	O	R	S	E
U	N	C	O	N	T	R	O	L	L	E	D	A	I
N	H	O	R	L	M	E	I	L	L	S	L	G	S
A	A	S	O	V	R	T	L	I	I	Y	I	U	A
E	R	I	I	M	I	I	N	L	A	R	V	I	T
S	M	T	E	S	R	U	M	M	T	B	E	L	N
P	I	N	N	H	B	I	A	O	O	G	U	T	A
G	N	A	T	G	N	I	G	G	A	R	B	S	F
S	I	G	N	D	I	F	F	E	R	E	N	C	E

CAN YOU NAME AN ITEM

THAT CAN KILL FOR EVERY LETTER OF THE ALPHABET

A ______________________________

B ______________________________

C ______________________________

D ______________________________

E ______________________________

F ______________________________

J ______________________________

H ______________________________

I ______________________________

J ______________________________

K ______________________________

L ______________________________

M ______________________________

CAN YOU NAME AN ITEM

THAT CAN KILL FOR EVERY LETTER OF THE ALPHABET

N ______

O ______

P ______

Q ______

R ______

S ______

T ______

U ______

V ______

W ______

X ______

Y ______

Z ______

LEVEL 3

The task is getting more and more difficult. This time, you need to save yourself from the angry beast as soon as possible. You are in the center of the labyrinth. How quickly will you be able to escape?

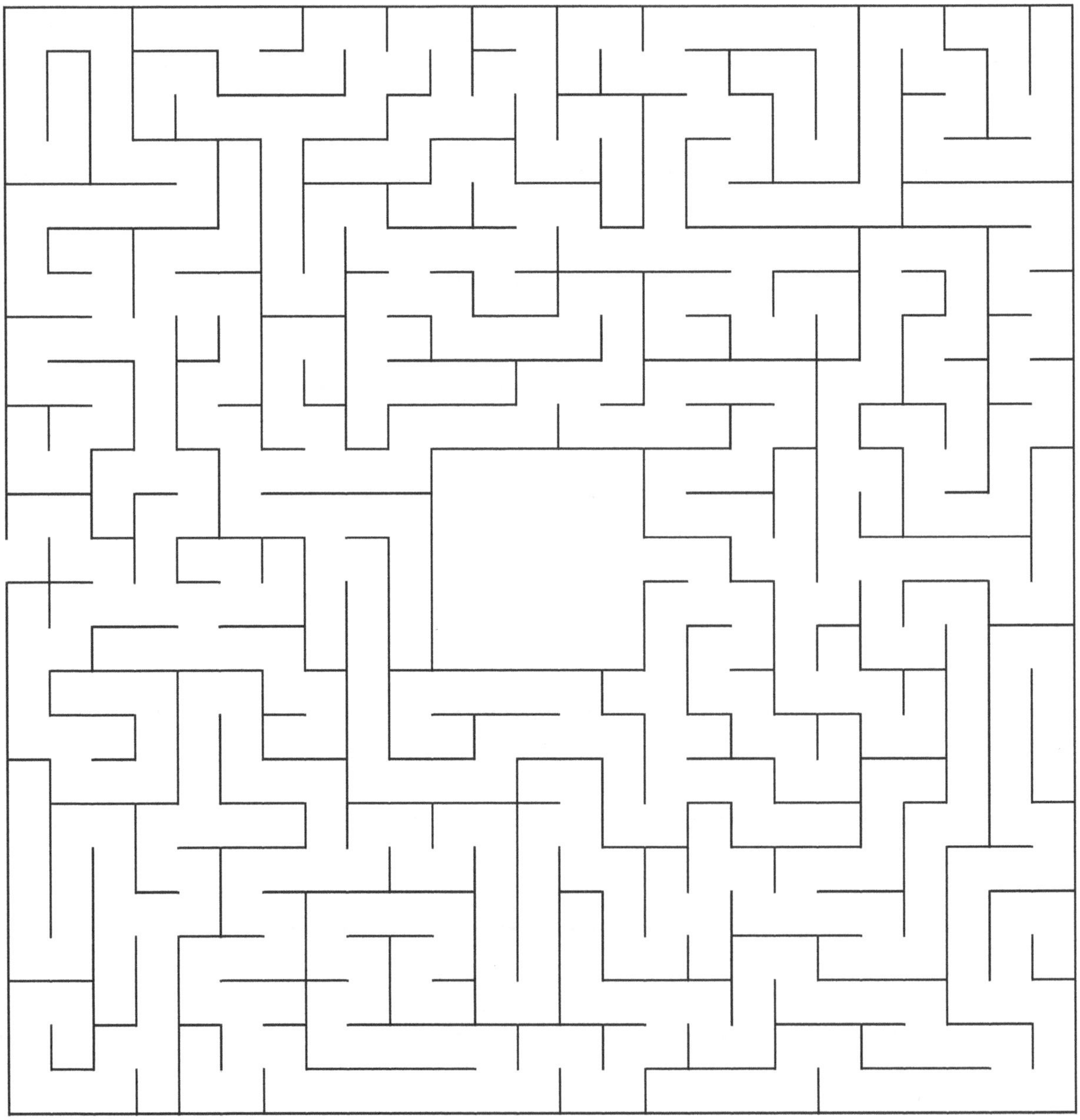

WHAT IS IN COMMON

BETWEEN BUNDY AND DAHMER?

1. ______________________________

2. ______________________________

3. ______________________________

4. ______________________________

5. ______________________________

6. ______________________________

7. ______________________________

CRYPTOGRAMS

A woman from a family of socially deprived people who lived in the forest, and is known as one of the most terrifying female murderers of our time...

Solve this cryptogram to find out the last words of Aileen.

A	B	C	D	E	F	G	H	I	J	K	L	M	N	O	P	Q	R	S	T	U	V	W	X	Y	Z

I' D   J U S T   L I K E   T O   S A Y

T O   U F D E   W T V P   E Z   D L J

_ ' _   _ _ _ _ _ _ _   _ _ _ _   _ _ _

T X   D L T W T Y R   H T E S   E S P

_ _ _ _   _ _ _   _ ' _ _   _ _   _ _ _ _

C Z N V   L Y O   T W W   M P   M L N V

FALLEN PHRASES!

"			■			,	■	T				■			R			■			■						N		■
			■					,	■	A		D	■			■				■		V			■				
								■			■				E	■				■				■			U	S	
	F	■				■						M						E		■	O		■					■	
■	■				■						.	"	■							■								■	■

				H										A			D		N							A			
		O		M	E		O		T	I				M			E		N			N	I	L	H	O			
O	U	P	A	S	N	D	D		N	O	N		S	M	I	L	C	W	T		E	U	O	T	N	I	T		T
H	T	W	T	E	V	E	L	I	H	G	U		O	T	Y	N	O	U	I		T	H	E	W	C	A	U	G	E
B	A	T	P	E	E	I	C	I	R	C	S	C	W	O	A	L	O	E	S	S	W	F	O	R	H	J	S	S	I

Oh no, not these facts again!

The Golden State Killer committed at least 13 murders between 1974 and 1986. He was known for breaking into his victims' houses, undressing and then standing at the entrance of their bedroom, tapping and scraping his long knife against the doorframe till they woke up.

SUDOKU

	4	9	1		3		2	
8		7	4			3		
		5						
			3			8		5
5	9		2			4		1
3		4	5	9				2
4		2	8	3	6	1	7	
7	8			2		6	5	
9						2		4

Oh no, not these facts again!

While in prison, Ed Kemper narrated hundreds of books on tape for blind people. Some of the most notable were "The Glass Key", "Flowers in the Attic", "Merlin's Mirror", "The Rosary Murders", and even "Star Wars"

COLORING PAGES
3 - 18+
WOODFIELD, RANDALL

TRUE CRIME WORD SEARCH

Find 20 words related to murder investigations

L	X	E	S	R	E	P	O	R	T	O	C	L	L
S	F	I	N	G	E	R	P	R	I	N	T	S	O
W	E	A	G	S	H	O	E	P	R	I	N	T	P
A	H	E	M	R	O	F	I	N	U	E	R	I	D
B	L	O	Y	C	A	M	E	R	A	E	N	E	E
S	O	E	R	Y	A	S	S	R	N	S	F	N	O
I	O	L	R	L	E	H	P	I	A	E	A	S	N
N	P	D	N	A	O	S	O	Y	N	R	A	U	C
Y	T	I	C	O	L	E	V	S	G	A	C	O	N
S	P	A	T	T	E	R	E	I	P	L	I	H	S
E	E	I	R	E	D	W	O	P	K	C	A	L	B
I	N	S	C	I	R	T	E	M	O	I	B	S	O
G	U	S	L	A	C	I	M	E	H	C	A	S	S
D	O	S	D	O	U	B	L	E	H	E	L	I	X

■	"			■					’		■			■					■			D	■						■
■			■			■		O			D		.	■		■				■		■				■			■
			…	K							■			M	E				Y	‘		■		■					
■		X						N			.	”	■							■	D	E		A	L			■	■

					I		S			G							O	A									R		
	A	N			R	A	L		U	N		S			L	A	R	D			N		L		T	U	N	N	
	E	I	T	E	T	L	S	N	C	T		S	O		D	B	E	R	D		A		S	O	C	V	O	F	
F	U	S	P	I	W	I	E	I	N	E		A	S	A	I	B	H	K	T	A	S		A	S	F	A	O	Y	Y

Oh no, not these facts again!

David Parker Ray, also known as the Toy-Box Killer, abducted and drugged his victims. He would play recordings to them of how he was going to torture them for the next 30 days whenever they woke up.

CRYPTOGRAMS

He is considered the meanest man on earth. On Panzram's conscience are more than 1,000 rapes of men and more than 20 victims. He never apologized, and more than once said that he would have committed even more crimes if he'd had the opportunity. Journalists called this serial killer too evil to live. This man must have said terrifying final words. Solve the cryptogram to find out what they were.

A	B	C	D	E	F	G	H	I	J	K	L	M	N	O	P	Q	R	S	T	U	V	W	X	Y	Z

HURRY IT UP YOU, _ _ _ _ _ _ _!

Z M J J Q   A L   M H   Q G M, T S K L S J V!

A U G M D V   Z S F Y   S   V G R W F

E W F   O Z A D W   Q G M ' J W

K U J W O A F Y   S J G M F V!

Connect letters to rearrange them into other words! Create as many words as you can

DONALD HENRY GASKINS

FALLEN PHRASES!

"	A	■		L				■			N	■				■					■				
■	■	■	■	■	■	■	■	■						R	"	■	■	■	■	■	■	■	■	■	■
■	■	■	■	■			H		■						■					■	■	■	■	■	■

U N

O O C A A Y E E A W Y

C J W N N M W R D G E T G A C A Y W I T H

Oh no, not these facts again!

There was a killer who wouldn't go into a house with a locked front door because, as he said, he "didn't feel welcome." Lock your doors, people!

TRUE CRIME WORD SEARCH

Find 20 American serial killers

R	A	D	E	R	S	E	N	O	J	C	S	F	F
D	N	L	H	M	G	A	C	Y	L	C	R	M	L
W	N	L	I	T	T	L	E	L	W	C	E	G	O
R	N	I	C	H	O	L	S	N	U	H	L	R	P
Z	E	R	I	M	A	R	A	B	O	I	H	E	E
N	B	G	O	E	R	M	H	A	R	K	G	P	Z
B	N	U	E	L	P	N	E	R	N	A	E	M	C
R	O	M	N	I	E	S	Z	N	O	T	I	E	A
I	A	F	H	D	C	R	O	A	S	I	N	K	K
D	A	S	I	O	Y	A	D	B	I	L	E	U	I
G	S	S	B	S	J	O	I	E	M	O	L	L	R
W	R	A	R	E	H	T	A	T	H	P	R	R	C
A	R	E	C	T	H	E	C	D	A	H	M	E	R
Y	R	D	R	E	B	E	R	K	O	W	I	T	Z

TRUE CRIME MEMES

THAT ABSOLUTELY DROVE OUR INSTAGRAM FOLLOWERS CRAZY

Oh no, not these facts again!

Ted Bundy was actively involved in politics, and there was talk that he may one day become the governor of Washington. Although he confessed to his lawyer that he had killed over a 100 people, he was only convicted of 30 murders.

SUDOKU

5					3	6	7	
		3	7		2	4		
8		9			6			
		8			1	5		
7	2							
6	9	1		4	7			
9		4		7	5			
3	5			1	4			
2	8	7	6	3		1		

Oh no, not these facts again!

Serial killer Robert Pickton put some of the bodies of his 49 victims through an industrial meat grinder and fed them to the pigs on his farm. He also mixed them with pork and sold it to meat processing businesses, family members, friends and even the local police.

Serial killers never ask permission from those who are kidnapped. But sometimes, they give victims an opportunity to escape with their quick wit and ingenuity. How about escaping from the center of the maze in two minutes? If you do it the first time, you have the capabilities of a secret agent.

Connect letters to rearrange them into other words! Create as many words as you can

THE GREEN RIVER KILLER

CRYPTOGRAMS

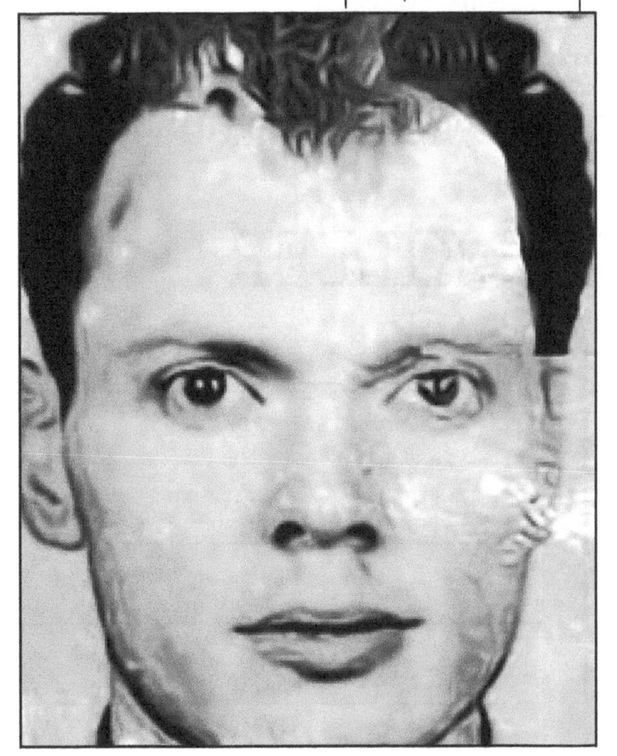

This man was the last to be electrocuted before America abolished capital punishment. Wanna know what he said at that moment?

Solve the cryptogram and find out.

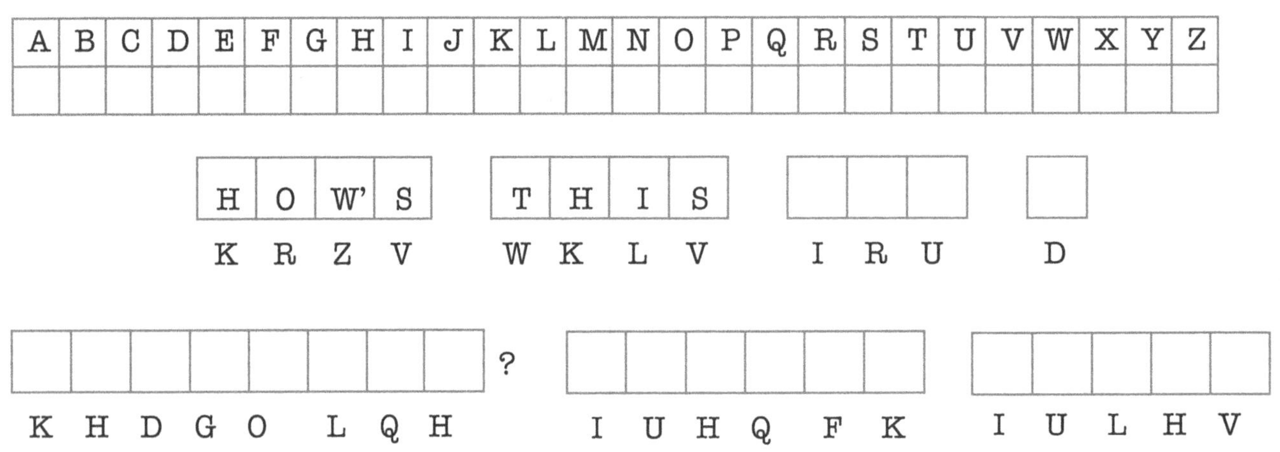

TRUE-CRIME WORD SEARCH

Find 20 things that can kill

A	M	P	E	R	A	G	E	N	R	E	A	X	E
H	E	I	G	H	T	R	O	P	E	S	O	L	T
B	L	O	O	D	L	O	S	S	T	R	I	N	G
W	A	S	N	I	A	H	C	T	M	A	R	E	R
E	A	K	C	O	R	R	E	E	H	I	O	E	T
O	C	U	U	E	S	R	I	M	F	H	M	L	C
R	I	S	S	O	A	A	D	L	M	M	S	I	O
P	D	R	L	D	E	C	E	R	A	E	N	D	R
S	E	O	O	A	G	L	H	H	F	O	W	P	S
A	D	R	U	G	S	T	I	M	S	I	B	T	D
B	T	O	A	G	P	H	D	I	I	A	R	E	S
E	M	H	G	E	P	T	O	O	T	H	O	E	A
R	S	E	D	R	R	P	E	N	U	G	G	A	F
C	L	O	T	H	E	S	L	I	N	E	M	L	S

TRUE CRIME MEMES
THAT ABSOLUTELY DROVE OUR INSTAGRAM FOLLOWERS CRAZY

Me Trying To Watch A Documentary
And Google The Killer's Biography At Once

Oh no, not these facts again!

Albert Fish wrote a letter to one of his victim's mothers, detailing how he had killed and eaten the 10-year-old girl. He described how sweet and tender she was, and how it had taken him nine days to consume the girl's body.

RIDDLES

Guess who committed this crime. Be attentive to the smallest details and remember the biographies of the most well-known serial killers!

KILLER'S NAME: ______________________________

Oh yes, you finally made it to the most difficult maze. I suggest you go through it with a friend. Schedule the time it takes you to get out of the center, and then check how long it takes your friend to do it. Whoever loses buys the beer!

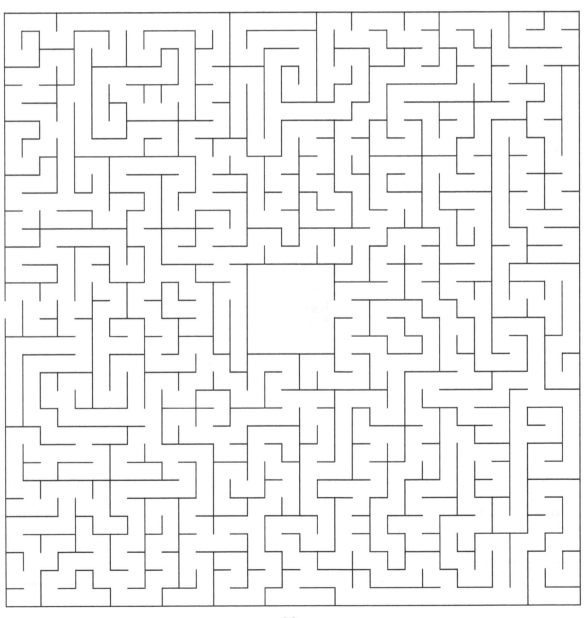

EXPRESS YOUR OPINION!

If you could choose only two cases to be solved, which ones would you choose and why?

1. ______________________________

2. ______________________________

COMMENT:

____

____

____

6			5				9	
		9		3				2
4	7	2	6	9		1		
				6		7		
1	5		2	4				
					9		3	
					4			
	8	1				5	4	
9	2	4				6		

Oh no, not these facts again!

Ed Kemper, also known as "The Butcher," recorded popular audio books like 'Flowers in The Attic' and 'Star Wars'.

AN OFFENSIVE NICKNAME FOR THESE SERIAL KILLERS

Toole Ottis ______________________

Unterweger Jack ______________________

Wuornos Aileen ______________________

Young Graham ______________________

Zodiac ______________________

Nichols Terry ______________________

Lavinia Fisher ______________________

Pickton Robert ______________________

Shawcross Arthur ______________________

Helen Golay ______________________

CAN YOU NAME SOMETHING

THAT WILL HELP DESTROY EVIDENCE FOR EVERY LETTER IN THE ALPHABET?

A ______________________________

B ______________________________

C ______________________________

D ______________________________

E ______________________________

F ______________________________

J ______________________________

H ______________________________

I ______________________________

J ______________________________

K ______________________________

L ______________________________

M ______________________________

CAN YOU NAME SOMETHING

THAT WILL HELP DESTROY EVIDENCE FOR EVERY LETTER IN THE ALPHABET?

N ______________________________

O ______________________________

P ______________________________

Q ______________________________

R ______________________________

S ______________________________

T ______________________________

U ______________________________

V ______________________________

W ______________________________

X ______________________________

Y ______________________________

Z ______________________________

Guess who committed this crime. Be attentive to the smallest details and remember the biographies of the most well-known serial killers!

KILLER'S NAME: ______________________________

EXPRESS YOUR OPINION

Remember the moment that you were carried away by true crime. What impressed you first?

TRUE CRIME MEMES

THAT ABSOLUTELY DROVE OUR INSTAGRAM FOLLOWERS CRAZY

Yep, I'm Sure That Your New Girlfriend Is Cool And Beautiful, But I Bet She Doesn't Know As Much About Ed Kemper As I Do

---

Oh no, not these facts again!

In the middle of his killing spree, Rodney Alcala, also known as "The Dating Game Killer," played and won an episode of **The Dating Game** in 1978.

FIND YOUR SERIAL KILLER NAME

First Letter Of The First Name

A CINNAMON
B RAILROAD
C POPS
D OCTAGON
E FROSTED
F FLOPHOUSE
G BRUN
H FROOTY
I BOXCAR
J KITCHEN
K CRISPY
L OUTBACK
M BACK ALLY
N THE BLOODY
O COCOA
P ICE CREAM TRUCK
Q CIRCUS
R BAY CITY
S PALTRY
T TERRIFYING
U IGLOO
V HANGER
W SCARY
X GARAGE SALE
Y MEAT LOCKER
Z STRIP MALL

First Letter Of The Last Name

A CHEF
B BUNNY
C FLAYER
D BOILER
E KILLER
F BUTCHER
G SLICER
H TICKLER
I CHEESE
J BODY THIEF
K KEEPER
L MONSTER
M SURGEON
N SMASHER
O FLAYER
P POISONER
Q MURDERER
R PICKLER
S STABBER
T DENTIST
U HACKER
V NURSE
W CANNIBAL
X CUTTER
Y KIDNAPPER
Z HANGMAN

____

____

CRYPTOGRAMS

The favorite of dozens of women, the most charming criminal in the world according to many fans of true crime, an insidious seducer with a monster hiding inside. Even leaving this life, he used the opportunity to attract attention one last time with an intriguing phrase. Solve this cryptogram to unravel his last words.

A	B	C	D	E	F	G	H	I	J	K	L	M	N	O	P	Q	R	S	T	U	V	W	X	Y	Z

I' D — L I K E — Y O U — _ _ — _ _ _ _

K F — N K M G — A Q W — V Q — I K X G

O A — N Q X G — V Q — O A — H C O K N A

C P F — H T K G P F U

Come up with the funniest serial killer rhymes.

Bundy ______________________________

Escobar ____________________________

Escobar ____________________________

Fish _______________________________

Pickton ____________________________

Oh no, not these facts again!

According to the Bureau of Justice Statistics, only 42% of violent crime are reported to authorities. Of that 42%, only 46% of cases are cleared. Therefore, less than a quarter of violent crimes get solved.

CROSSWORDS

ACROSS:

2. What serial killer sent letters to local newspapers, signing them with a pseudonym and brand name?

4. What kind of surgery did Jeffrey Dahmer perform on his victims at home?

5. How many confirmed murders with famous victim names did Aileen Wuornos commit?

DOWN:

1. Last name of the serial killer who stored the bodies of the victims on his family's pig farm

3. The surname of a serial killer whose nickname was "The Co-Ed Butcher"

COLORING PAGES
URDIALES, ANDREW
8

KENWORTH

Guess who committed this crime. Be attentive to the smallest details and remember the biographies of the most well-known serial killers!

KILLER'S NAME: ______________________________

LEVEL 6

Only a real pro can complete this level in a matter of minutes. Can you prove that you can be considered one of them?

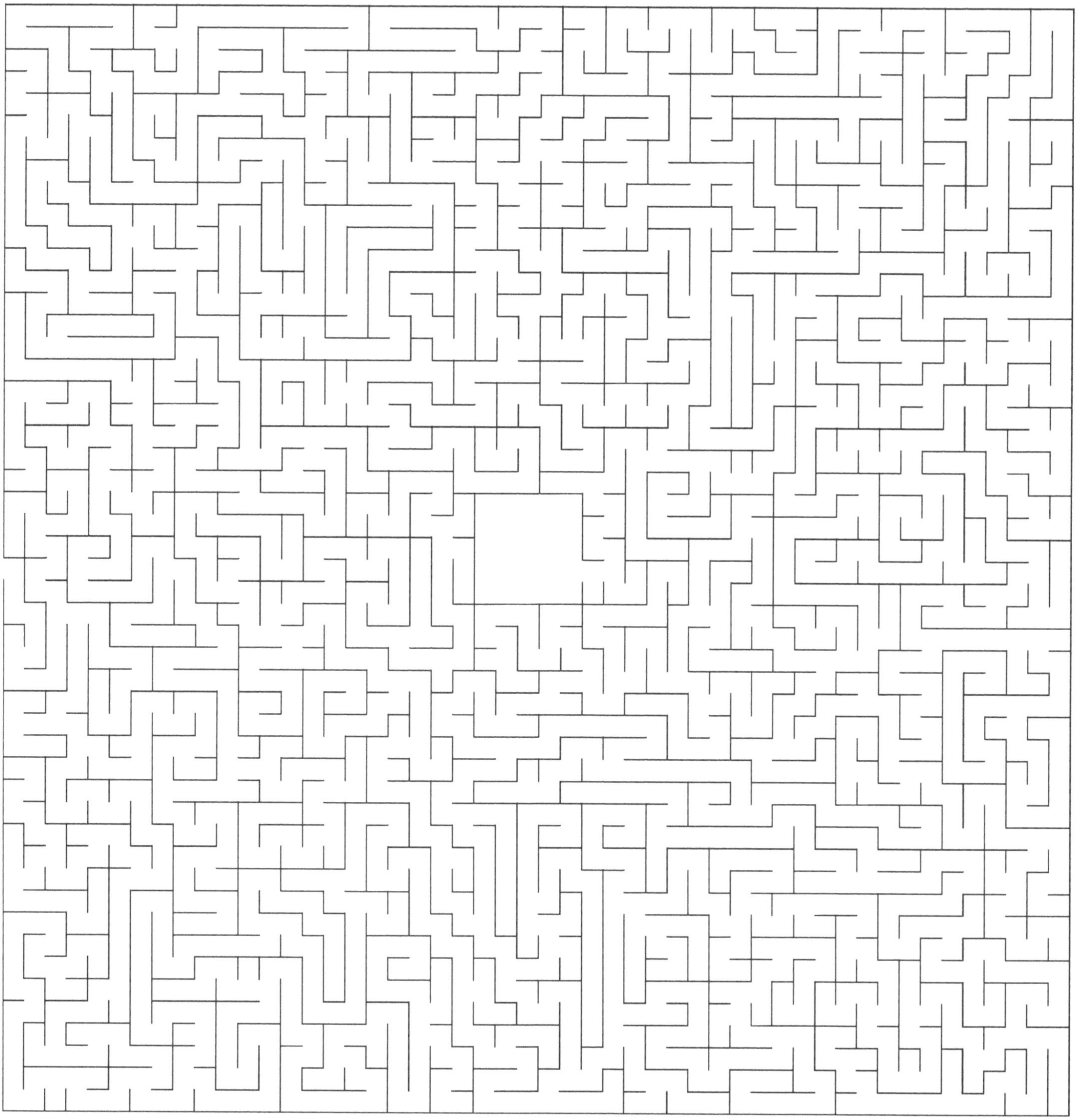

TRUE CRIME WORD SEARCH

Find 20 words related to murder investigations

I	U	Y	T	N	I	R	P	R	E	G	N	I	F
T	A	R	E	L	A	N	I	M	I	R	C	I	S
S	N	O	V	B	V	A	R	E	B	T	R	N	F
A	A	T	I	F	V	N	O	N	N	R	I	V	I
I	L	A	D	P	B	E	R	E	E	E	M	E	L
U	Y	R	E	N	A	I	M	V	E	V	E	S	E
N	S	O	N	N	R	E	O	E	F	O	S	T	S
U	I	B	C	E	C	C	B	E	R	C	C	I	M
G	S	A	E	R	R	E	D	L	D	N	E	G	O
I	B	L	O	E	C	E	A	I	O	U	N	A	T
E	R	F	D	I	R	T	L	I	R	O	E	T	I
I	N	N	L	A	R	R	E	S	T	E	D	I	V
E	U	O	L	E	S	N	E	P	S	U	S	O	E
R	P	N	G	N	G	T	N	E	G	A	R	N	O

COLORING PAGES
10
Ford
Gallego
Gerald & Charlene

TRUE CRIME MEMES
THAT ABSOLUTELY DROVE OUR INSTAGRAM FOLLOWERS CRAZY

My Family Trying
To Watch Movie In Calm

Me Explaining Serial Killer's
Biography In Details

MATH LOGIC

Are you good at math? Solve this true crime riddle

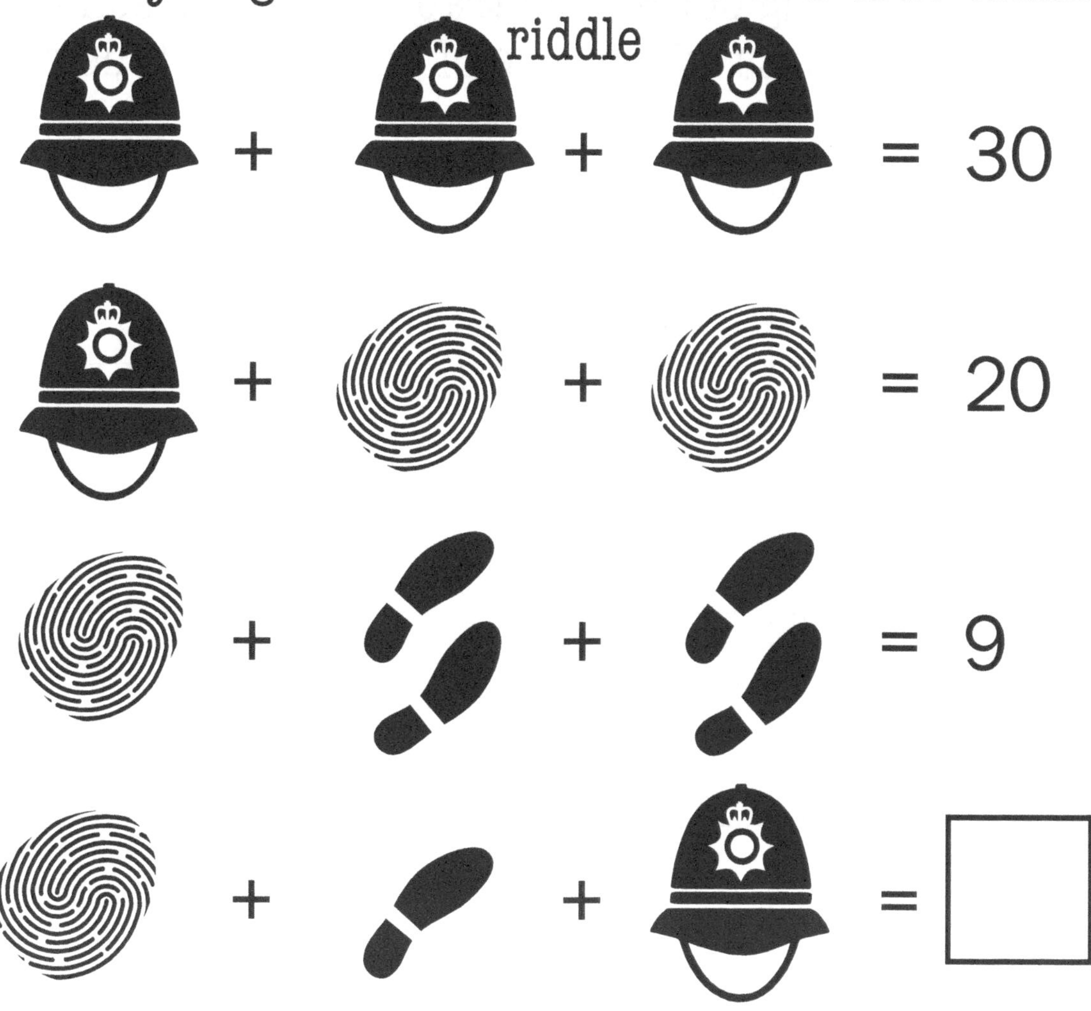

THE ANSWER IS ______________________________

Oh no, not these facts again!

Imagine a serial killer's victim; what picture came to mind? A woman? This is not surprising, as women are often portrayed as the victims in movies, and most of the victims of gruesome crimes are women, although, 53.8% of the serial killers are men.

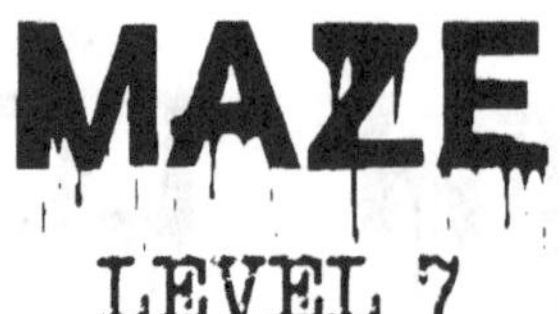

LEVEL 7

How about getting out of this trap? Time yourself and compare your results with those of your fellow true crime fan.

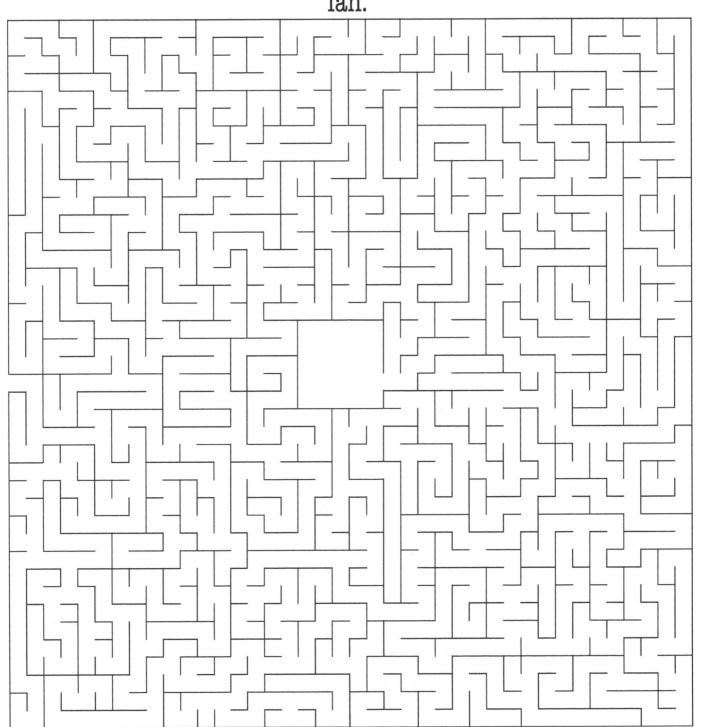

TRUE-CRIME WORD SEARCH

Find 20 female serial killers

U	D	G	S	Y	R	E	H	S	I	F	O	E	G
Z	A	L	D	E	I	R	F	T	T	O	G	E	I
N	I	N	N	B	H	W	E	S	T	R	O	T	L
S	U	U	S	E	D	B	U	Y	C	B	B	B	B
B	R	N	D	N	E	T	O	O	H	A	A	E	E
B	L	E	Y	D	N	L	H	G	R	R	T	S	R
S	A	E	E	E	B	R	R	A	I	N	H	R	T
S	Z	R	R	R	E	E	H	H	S	A	O	A	O
O	A	K	F	E	T	I	A	I	H	B	R	S	P
D	R	I	E	I	N	F	S	K	I	E	Y	E	P
S	R	N	N	D	E	D	R	C	K	T	A	W	A
N	A	N	L	E	U	L	U	E	A	B	S	H	N
A	B	E	P	T	P	N	D	B	W	I	I	O	B
G	Y	L	T	B	U	E	N	O	A	N	O	E	H

I WISH I DIDN'T KNOW

THAT TESTS

According to
unconfirmed reports, how many girls were raped
and
killed by serial killer Pedro Alonso Lopez,
who was secretly released instead of a
well-deserved execution due to “good
behavior”?

a. Over 110

b. More than 230

c. More than 300

TRUE CRIME MEMES
THAT ABSOLUTELY DROVE OUR INSTAGRAM FOLLOWERS CRAZY

When I Finally Get Home After A Busy Day And Start Watching Documentaries About Serial Killers

---

Oh no, not these facts again!

The FBI keeps a list of serial killings by state. While the list of serial killers per capita consists mostly of states in the south west, it's cold, snowy Alaska that takes the top spot. While there have been only 51 serial killings in the history of the state, that's nearly sixteen people per million.

WORD SCRAMBLE

Unjumble the scrambled letters to make surnames of the serial killers with the largest number of victims

1. LETTLI ____________________

2. RWADYIG ____________________

3. VERYHA ____________________

4. BAEANBTR ____________________

5. HDMRAE ____________________

6. ENGRE ____________________

7. KEREPM ____________________

Oh no, not these facts again!

Once, the BTK killer got frustrated and left one of his next victim's home because she was running late.

ANSWER KEYS

I WISH I DIDN'T KNOW

THAT TESTS

Page	
9	a. Video and sound of her voice
14	b. Cooked and ate
22	c. Dennis Rader
34	c. 40 years
49	a. If God wanted her found, she would be found
59	c. It tastes like shit

ANSWER KEYS

MAZE

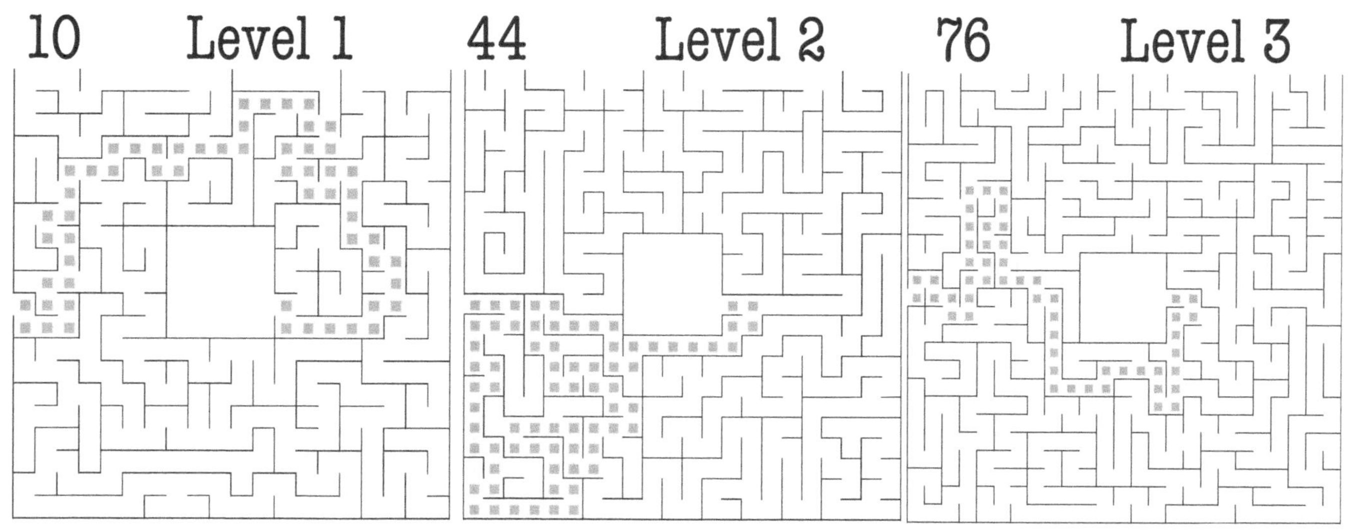
10 Level 1
44 Level 2
76 Level 3

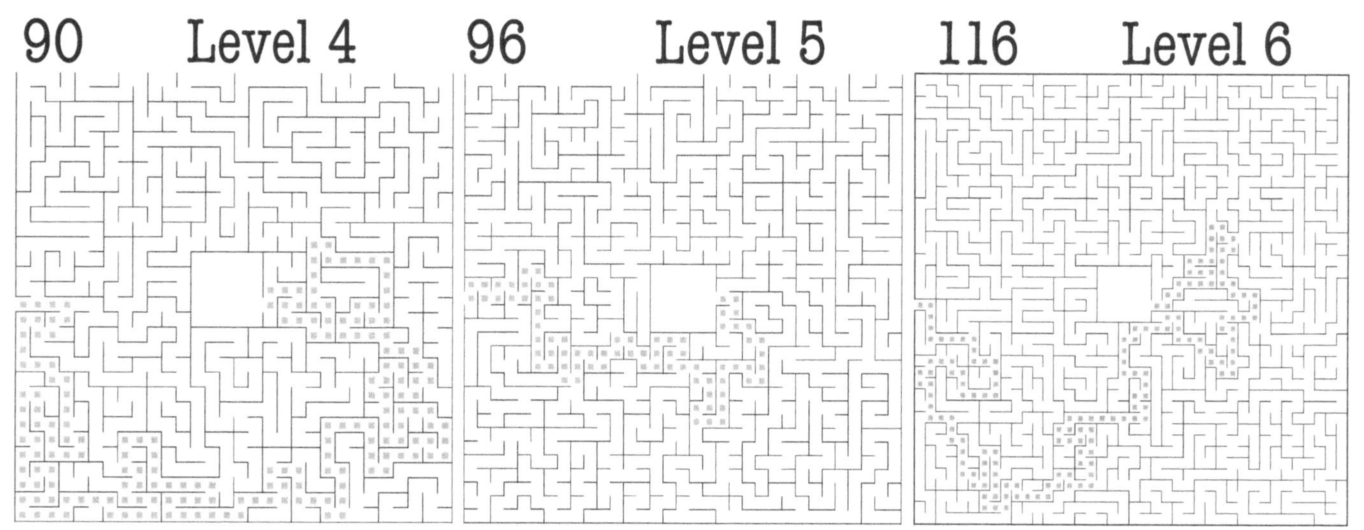
90 Level 4
96 Level 5
116 Level 6

ANSWER KEYS

SUDOKU

12

1	9	7	8	3	4	5	6	2
5	2	4	1	9	6	7	3	8
3	8	6	7	5	2	9	4	1
6	4	1	2	8	5	3	7	9
2	5	3	4	7	9	1	8	6
9	7	8	3	6	1	4	2	5
4	6	2	9	1	3	8	5	7
7	3	9	5	2	8	6	1	4
8	1	5	6	4	7	2	9	3

31

4	2	7	5	1	3	9	8	6
9	6	3	8	2	4	1	7	5
1	8	5	7	9	6	3	4	2
5	9	4	6	3	1	7	2	8
6	7	1	2	8	9	4	5	3
2	3	8	4	7	5	6	1	9
3	4	2	1	6	8	5	9	7
7	5	9	3	4	2	8	6	1
8	1	6	9	5	7	2	3	4

54

3	2	1	6	7	9	5	8	4
5	8	7	1	3	4	2	9	6
9	6	4	8	5	2	1	7	3
4	5	3	9	8	1	6	2	7
1	7	6	4	2	5	9	3	8
2	9	8	7	6	3	4	5	1
6	1	5	3	9	7	8	4	2
7	4	2	5	1	8	3	6	9
8	3	9	2	4	6	7	1	5

72

2	6	8	4	1	5	7	9	3
3	4	9	2	7	8	5	6	1
1	7	5	9	3	6	2	8	4
9	2	6	3	8	7	1	4	5
4	8	7	5	2	1	9	3	6
5	3	1	6	9	4	8	7	2
7	9	3	1	6	2	4	5	8
6	1	4	8	5	9	3	2	7
8	5	2	7	4	3	6	1	9

ANSWER KEYS

SUDOKU

80

6	4	9	1	8	3	5	2	7
8	2	7	4	5	9	3	1	6
1	3	5	6	7	2	9	4	8
2	7	6	3	4	1	8	9	5
5	9	8	2	6	7	4	3	1
3	1	4	5	9	8	7	6	2
4	5	2	8	3	6	1	7	9
7	8	1	9	2	4	6	5	3
9	6	3	7	1	5	2	8	4

89

5	4	2	1	9	3	6	7	8
1	6	3	7	8	2	4	9	5
8	7	9	4	5	6	2	1	3
4	3	8	9	2	1	5	6	7
7	2	5	3	6	8	9	4	1
6	9	1	5	4	7	3	8	2
9	1	4	2	7	5	8	3	6
3	5	6	8	1	4	7	2	9
2	8	7	6	3	9	1	5	4

98

6	3	8	5	1	2	4	9	7
5	1	9	4	3	7	8	6	2
4	7	2	6	9	8	1	5	3
2	9	3	8	6	5	7	1	4
1	5	7	2	4	3	9	8	6
8	4	6	1	7	9	2	3	5
7	6	5	9	8	4	3	2	1
3	8	1	7	2	6	5	4	9
9	2	4	3	5	1	6	7	8

ANSWER KEYS

RIDDLES

18 Edmund Kemper

29 David Berkowitz

52 Elmer Wayne Henley

95 Ramirez Richard

102 John Wayne Gacy

110 Gary Ridgway

47 Pisces, Gemini, Sagittarius, and Virgo are the most common zodiac signs among serial killers, according to an astrologer.

ANSWER KEYS

FALLEN PHRASES!

21 "I BELIEVE THE ONLY WAY TO REFORM PVEOPLE IS TO KILL THEM."
CARL PANZRAM

68 "I ACTUALLY THINK I MAY BE POSSESSED WITH DEMONS... I WAS DROPPED ON MY HEAD AS A KID."
DENNIS RADER

79 "TO ME, THIS WORLD IS NOTHING BUT EVIL, AND MY OWN EVIL JUST HAPPENED TO COME OUT THE CAUSE OF THE CIRCUMSTANCES OF WHAT I WAS DOING." AILEEN WUORNOS

83 "IT WASN'T AS DARK AND SCARY AS IT SOUNDS, I HAD A LOT OF FUN...KILLING SOMEBODY'S A FUNNY EXPERIENCE." ALBERT DESALVO

86 "A CLOWN CAN GET AWAY WITH MURDER"
JOHN WAYNE GACY

ANSWER KEYS

CROSSWORDS

23

DOWN:

1. The Boston ... was a nickname of Albert de Salvo (STRANGLER)

4. Which serial killer was the inspiration for the murderous character Scorpio in the 1971 film Dirty Harry? (ZODIAC)

ACROSS:

2. How old was Edmund Kemper when he first committed murder? (SIXTEEN)

3. The surname of a serial killer which Ted Bundy aided detectives in capturing (RIDGWAY)

5. What is Ted Bundy's education? (PSYCHOLOGIST)

ACROSS:

2. What serial killer sent letters to local newspapers, singing them with a pseudonym and brand name? (ZODIAC)

4. What kind of surgery does Jeffrey Dahmer perform on his victims at home? (LOBOTOMY)

5How many confimed murders with famous victim names did Aileen Wuornos commit? (SEVEN)

DOWN:

1. Last name of the serial killer who stored the bodies of the victims on his family pig farm (PICKTON)

3. The surname of a serial killer whose nickname was "The Co-Ed Butcher" (KEMPER)

ANSWER KEYS

WORD SCRAMBLE

25

Barfield
Barnabet
Beck
Bender
Brown
Buenoano
Bundy

48

LOSANGELES
MIAMI
ALASKA
MANCHESTER
NEWMEXICO
TENNESSEE
ARKANSAS
NEVADA
LOUISIANA
MISSOURI

28

GARAVITO
LOPEZ IQBAL
POPKOV
BARBOSA
FILHO
SHANKARIYA

120

LITTLE
RIDGEWAY
HARVEY
BARNABET
DAHMER
GREEN
KEMPER

ANSWER KEYS

CRYPTOGRAMS

30

A	B	C	D	E	F	G	H	I	J	K	L	M	N	O	P	Q	R	S	T	U	V	W	X	Y	Z
H	I	J	K	L	M	N	O	P	Q	R	S	T	U	V	W	X	Y	Z	A	B	C	D	E	F	G

I DON'T CARE IF I
P KVUA JHYL PM P

LIVE OR DIE GO AHEAD
SPCL VY KPL NV HOLHK

AND KILL ME
HUK RPSS TL

41

A	B	C	D	E	F	G	H	I	J	K	L	M	N	O	P	Q	R	S	T	U	V	W	X	Y	Z
W	X	Y	Z	A	B	C	D	E	F	G	H	I	J	K	L	M	N	O	P	Q	R	S	T	U	V

KISS MY ASS
GEOO IU WOO

67

A	B	C	D	E	F	G	H	I	J	K	L	M	N	O	P	Q	R	S	T	U	V	W	X	Y	Z
K	L	M	N	O	P	Q	R	S	T	U	V	W	X	Y	Z	A	B	C	D	E	F	G	H	I	J

WELL, GENTLEMEN, YOU
GOVV, QOXDVOWOX, IYE

ARE ABOUT TO SEE A
KOB KLYED DY COO K

BAKED APPEL
LKUON KZZOV

ANSWER KEYS

CRYPTOGRAMS

78

A	B	C	D	E	F	G	H	I	J	K	L	M	N	O	P	Q	R	S	T	U	V	W	X	Y	Z
L	M	N	O	P	Q	R	S	T	U	V	W	X	Y	Z	A	B	C	D	E	F	G	H	I	J	K

I'D JUST LIKE TO SAY
TO UFDE WTVP EZ DLJ

I'M SAILING WITH THE
TX DLTWTYR HTES ESP

ROCK AND I'LL BE BACK
CZNV LYO TWW MP MLNV

84

A	B	C	D	E	F	G	H	I	J	K	L	M	N	O	P	Q	R	S	T	U	V	W	X	Y	Z
S	T	U	V	W	X	Y	Z	A	B	C	D	E	F	G	H	I	J	K	L	M	N	O	P	Q	R

HURRY IT UP YOU
ZMJJQ AL MH QGM

BASTARD! I COULD HANG
TSKLSJV A UGMDV ZSFY

A DOZEN MEN WHILE
S VGRWF EWF OZADW

YOU'RE SCREWING
QGMJW KUJWOAFY

AROUND!
SJGMFV

ANSWER KEYS

CRYPTOGRAMS

92

A	B	C	D	E	F	G	H	I	J	K	L	M	N	O	P	Q	R	S	T	U	V	W	X	Y	Z
D	E	F	G	H	I	J	K	L	M	N	O	P	Q	R	S	T	U	V	W	X	Y	Z	A	B	C

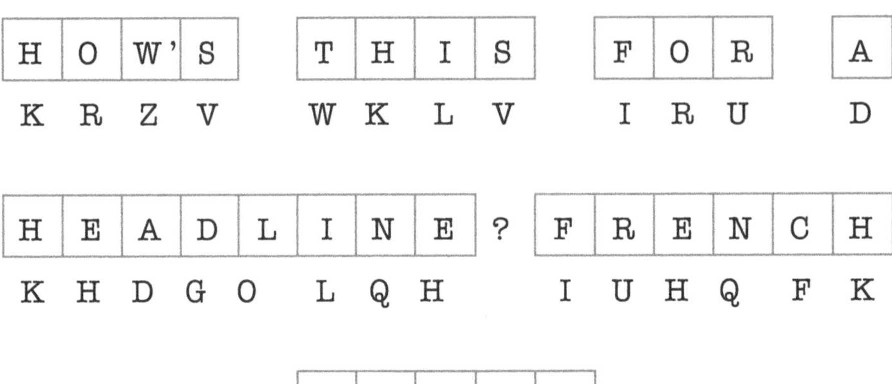

H O W' S T H I S F O R A
K R Z V W K L V I R U D
H E A D L I N E ? F R E N C H
K H D G O L Q H I U H Q F K
F R I E S
I U L H V

106

A	B	C	D	E	F	G	H	I	J	K	L	M	N	O	P	Q	R	S	T	U	V	W	X	Y	Z
C	D	E	F	G	H	I	J	K	L	M	N	O	P	Q	R	S	T	U	V	W	X	Y	Z	A	B

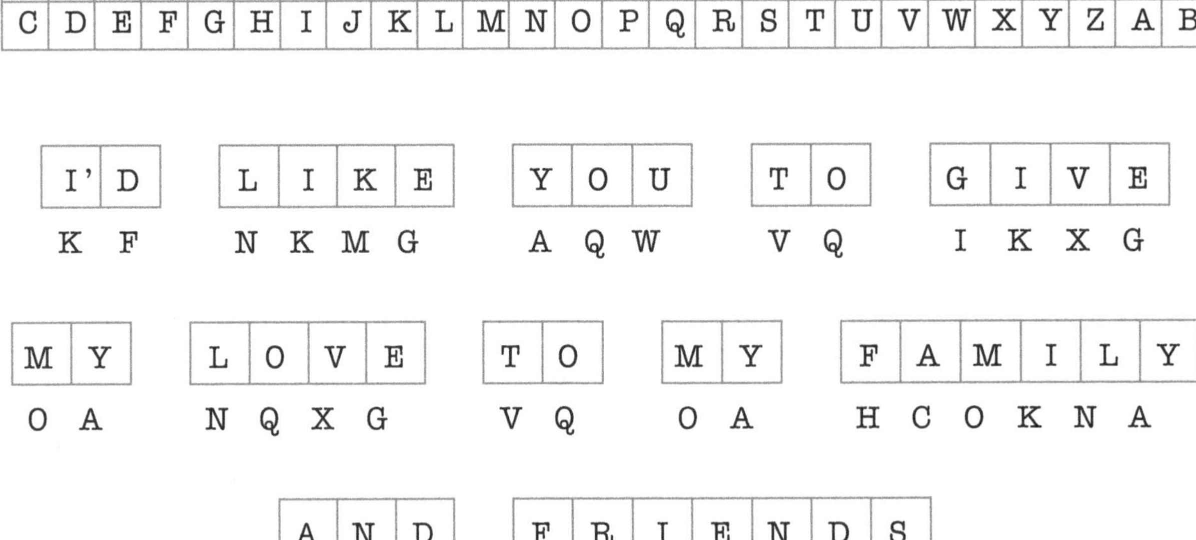

I' D L I K E Y O U T O G I V E
K F N K M G A Q W V Q I K X G
M Y L O V E T O M Y F A M I L Y
O A N Q X G V Q O A H C O K N A
A N D F R I E N D S
C P F H T K G P F U

ANSWER KEYS

TRUE-CRIME WORD SEARCH

36

```
N S S R J D L I L S G H C C
E R S K I N E K N O T L R A
D L E I F D O O W O O E I C
O N O S N I B O R O O E O N
T D S I N M B H L L R O C A
B A N J O A S H I P M A N M
N O S D H S F L E K L S R Y
L K T A O S D I S D T N J D
S T T R G G N O L S V E I N
R J N U E O E L S O O M L A
D T M S L A P E T I O T E C
A F S O D S E M O A R A A L
P M S M I L A T S L I V K O
D M L K E Y E S L G F I E Y
```

73

```
N M A N I P U L A T I V E N
P A A C D E C E I T F U L O
T R S I B C O Y H T A P M E
G S L U E V I S L U P M I L
L O A C A L L O U S N E S S
I N I P N A N R E M O R S E
U N C O N T R O L L E D A I
N H O R L M E I L L S L G S
A A S O V R T L I I Y I U A
E R I I M I I N L A R V I T
S M T E S R U M M T B E L N
P I N N H B I A O O G U T A
G N A T G N I G G A R B S F
S G I N D I F F E R E N C E
```

62

```
M T E V K I D N A P P I N G
U U S P T I E C P O H T R E
R Y A D B P A B O D Y I M L
D R C A N P T A Y P I A L A
E A D N D I H N L R Y O S T
R C L G C R I M E O N C I E
B S O E L E S E I I E L A N
L N C R P B L S M E V U K T
O R H R L B E U E E I S C P
O N O T I E L R S M L S V R
D S E R I A L K I L L E R I
L R R E F I N K O L T E L N
I E E J U S T I C E N S N T
T B D S N B K C T S E R R A
```

82

```
L X E S R E P O R T O C L L
S F I N G E R P R I N T S O
W E A G S H O E P R I N T P
A H E M R O F I N U E R I D
B L O Y C A M E R A E N E E
S O E R Y A S S R N S F N O
I O L R L E H P I A E A S N
N P D N A O S O Y N R A U C
Y T I C O L E V S G A C O N
S P A T T E R E I P L I H S
E E I R E D W O P K C A L B
I N S C I R T E M O I B S O
G U S L A C I M E H C A S S
D O S D O U B L E H E L I X
```

ANSWER KEYS

TRUE-CRIME WORD SEARCH

87

R	A	D	E	R	S	E	N	O	J	C	S	F	F
D	N	L	H	M	G	A	C	Y	L	C	R	M	L
W	N	L	I	T	T	L	E	L	W	C	E	G	O
R	N	I	C	H	O	L	S	N	U	H	L	R	P
Z	E	R	I	M	A	R	A	B	O	I	H	E	E
N	B	G	O	E	R	M	H	A	R	K	G	P	Z
B	N	U	E	L	P	N	E	R	N	A	E	M	C
R	O	M	N	I	E	S	Z	N	O	T	I	E	A
I	A	F	H	D	C	R	O	A	S	I	N	K	K
D	A	S	I	O	Y	A	D	B	I	L	E	U	I
G	S	S	B	S	J	O	I	E	M	O	L	L	R
W	R	A	R	E	H	T	A	T	H	P	R	R	C
A	R	E	C	T	H	E	C	D	A	H	M	E	R
Y	R	D	R	E	B	E	R	K	O	W	I	T	Z

112

I	U	Y	T	N	I	R	P	R	E	G	N	I	F
T	A	R	E	L	A	N	I	M	I	R	C	I	S
S	N	O	V	B	V	A	R	E	B	T	R	N	F
A	A	T	I	F	V	N	O	N	N	R	I	V	I
I	L	A	D	P	B	E	R	E	E	E	M	E	L
U	Y	R	E	N	A	I	M	V	E	V	E	S	E
N	S	O	N	N	R	E	O	E	F	O	S	T	S
U	I	B	C	E	C	C	B	E	R	C	C	I	M
G	S	A	E	R	R	E	D	L	D	N	E	G	O
I	B	L	O	E	C	E	A	I	O	U	N	A	T
E	R	F	D	I	R	T	L	I	R	O	E	T	I
I	N	N	L	A	R	R	E	S	T	E	D	I	V
E	U	O	L	E	S	N	E	P	S	U	S	O	E
R	P	N	G	N	G	T	N	E	G	A	R	N	O

93

A	M	P	E	R	A	G	E	N	R	E	A	X	E
H	E	I	G	H	T	R	O	P	E	S	O	L	T
B	L	O	O	D	L	O	S	S	T	R	I	N	G
W	A	S	N	I	A	H	C	T	M	A	R	E	R
E	A	K	C	O	R	R	E	E	H	I	O	E	T
O	C	U	U	E	S	R	I	M	F	H	M	L	C
R	I	S	S	O	A	A	D	L	M	M	S	I	O
P	D	R	L	D	E	C	E	R	A	E	N	D	R
S	E	O	O	A	G	L	H	H	F	O	W	P	S
A	D	R	U	G	S	T	I	M	S	I	B	T	D
B	T	O	A	G	P	H	D	I	I	A	R	E	S
E	M	H	G	E	P	T	O	O	T	H	O	E	A
R	S	E	D	R	R	P	E	N	U	G	G	A	F
C	L	O	T	H	E	S	L	I	N	E	M	L	S

117

U	D	G	S	Y	R	E	H	S	I	F	O	E	G
Z	A	L	D	E	I	R	F	T	T	O	G	E	I
N	I	N	N	B	H	W	E	S	T	R	O	T	L
S	U	U	S	E	D	B	U	Y	C	B	B	B	B
B	R	N	D	N	E	T	O	O	H	A	A	E	E
B	L	E	Y	D	N	L	H	G	R	R	T	S	R
S	A	E	E	E	B	R	R	A	I	N	H	R	T
S	Z	R	R	R	E	E	H	H	S	A	O	A	O
O	A	K	F	E	T	I	A	I	H	B	R	S	P
D	R	I	E	I	N	F	S	K	I	E	Y	E	P
S	R	N	N	D	E	D	R	C	K	T	A	W	A
N	A	N	L	E	U	L	U	E	A	B	S	H	N
A	B	E	P	T	P	N	D	B	W	I	I	O	B
G	Y	L	T	B	U	E	N	O	A	N	O	E	H

ANSWER KEYS

LOGIC

16 **15**

32 **15**

46 **60**

20 **15**

115 **16**